Puffin Books

Napper's Luck

Napper McCann, De
team, Warne County
Division of the Brontle
Championship, the Lea
Cup, there's everything

But in the very first game the team's star goalie is injured and is out for the rest of the season. When their second goalie is also injured, Colts find themselves struggling. Has Napper's luck run out in this thrilling sixth book of the series about his football career?

Martin Waddell has played football nearly all his life, and as a teenager was an apprentice goalkeeper for Fulham. He was born and educated in Northern Ireland and has written a great number of books, both for children and adults. He also writes under the pen-name Catherine Sefton, and many of these titles have Irish settings. He lives in County Down with his wife and three sons.

Other books by Martin Waddell

NAPPER GOES FOR GOAL
NAPPER STRIKES AGAIN
NAPPER'S GOLDEN GOALS
NAPPER'S BIG MATCH
NAPPER SUPER-SUB

TALES FROM THE SHOP THAT NEVER
  SHUTS

For younger readers

CLASS THREE AND THE BEANSTALK
THE GHOST FAMILY ROBINSON
THE GHOST FAMILY ROBINSON AT
  THE SEASIDE
HERBIE WHISTLE
THE LUCKY DUCK SONG

Picture Books

GOING WEST (with Philippe Dupasquier)
MAN MOUNTAIN (with Claudio Muñoz)

Books by Catherine Sefton

ALONG A LONELY ROAD
BERTIE BOGGIN AND THE GHOST
  AGAIN!
THE GHOST AND BERTIE BOGGIN

For younger readers

THE HAUNTED SCHOOLBAG

Martin Waddell

Napper's Luck

Illustrated by Michael Strand

Puffin Books

For Paul Scott Cree, who sent me his stories

PUFFIN BOOKS

Published by the Penguin Group
Penguin Books Ltd, 27 Wrights Lane, London w8 5tz, England
Penguin Books USA Inc., 375 Hudson Street, New York, New York 10014, USA
Penguin Books Australia Ltd, Ringwood, Victoria, Australia
Penguin Books Canada Ltd, 10 Alcorn Avenue, Toronto, Ontario, Canada m4v 3b2
Penguin Books (NZ) Ltd, 182–190 Wairau Road, Auckland 10, New Zealand

Penguin Books Ltd, Registered Offices: Harmondsworth, Middlesex, England

Published in Puffin Books 1993
10 9 8 7 6 5 4 3 2 1

The moral right of the author has been asserted

Typeset by Datix International Limited, Bungay, Suffolk
Filmset in Monophoto Baskerville
Printed in England by Clays Ltd, St Ives plc

Contents

1. League Champions?

This is the Warne County Colts Squad before our first game in the newly formed Brontley League Premier Division against Allentown at King's Court Stadium. County had leased the ground for our home games.

Tommy Cowans, our Team Manager, had added two players to the squad that played in the Western Area Qualifying Competition and got us into the Brontley League Premier Division. Chris Taggert was brought in as an extra defender from Carncross Rovers, and Marty Legget was signed from Bassett. Marty was their top scorer, but he had only scored six goals in twenty games in the Zaniger League, so that didn't mean much. Bassett were put into Division Two of the new Brontley League, so the signing was a move up for Marty. Tommy thought he had the makings of a good player.

Our squad of sixteen players was:

Keepers: Tony Bantam, Ally Scott.
Backs: Tom Brocken, 'Robbo' Robinson,
Cyril Small, Ronnie Purdy, Chris Taggert.

Midfield: Harpur Brown, Joe Fish,
'Alex' Alexiou.

Strikers: Andy 'Jezzer' Jezz, Danny Mole,
'Napper' McCann, 'Matty' Matthews,
Lester Singh, Marty Legget.

Roughly that was it, anyway. Several people had switched around during the Qualifying Competition, with Danny Mole playing a bit at the back, and Ronnie starting off in midfield, and only dropping back when we signed Harpur Brown. Then there were players like Alexiou, who could play almost anywhere. Tommy said he felt we had a good squad.

'The League Rules say we can have up to eighteen signed players,' he warned us. 'But the purpose of this competition is to get you all *playing*. I don't want to sign kids up, and then have them standing on the touch-line. There will be changes in the team, from week to week, to make sure that everyone has their chance. We will see how things work out and, if need be, new players can be brought in.'

That seemed fair enough to everybody. With

twelve teams in the League we would have twenty-two League games, and there would be the Open Cup and League Cup Competitions as well. Even if Tommy didn't want to make changes, he would probably have to, with injuries and suspensions, and people getting colds in their big toes.

The teams in the Premier Division were:

Olympic YC
Warne County Colts
Queenstown
Silvertown
Scottown Albion
BYC
Allentown United
Carncross Rovers
Celthill
Swans
Vale United
Kings Aston

We knew all about Olympic YC and Queenstown because we had played against them in the Western Qualifying Competition, and Chris Taggert had come from Carncross Rovers, where he couldn't get a place, so we knew about them, but the other teams were more or less a mystery. BYC, Kings Aston and Allentown had won their sections, so we thought they would probably be hot stuff, but the Qualifying Competitions weren't a good guide.

'There will be players dropped out because they are over the age limit,' Tommy told us. 'And teams like Olympic had the advantage of having played together before the Qualifying Competition . . . that has been evened out now. To begin with, we just take each game as it comes.'

'And win it!' Cyril Small shouted from the back, doing his cheer-leader act.

Tommy frowned and waited for him to shut up.

Cyril shut up then.

It didn't stop him blowing about how we were the Wonder Team that was going to walk the Premier Division first time out, and win both the cups. He went round boasting to everyone, which is typical Cyril Small. Then, when the team for our opening League game was picked, Cyril wasn't in it, which is typical Tommy!

When the team list went up in the dressing-room, old Cyril was like a burst balloon. One minute he was playing tricks on people and kidding about playing for Manchester United, and the next he was standing there with his mouth open.

'Hard luck, Cyril,' Mr Hope said.

'Not even sub!' Cyril grumbled.

Mr Hope knows us both well. He was headmaster at the school Cyril and Harpur and I went to, and he ran the school football team, Red Row Stars. He knew the manager of Warne County First Team, George Trotman, and it was through Mr Hope that we ended up signing on for Warne County Colts.

Mr Hope brings us over in his car to Owen Lane for training on Wednesday nights because the buses are awkward.

'Tommy has to pick a team,' Mr Hope said. 'He knows all about you. Just stick in there and don't lose heart, and you'll get your chance to win your place back.'

'I wanted to be in the team,' Cyril said.

There was no use trying to cheer him up, though if he had known what was going to happen in our first match against Allentown, he might have felt differently.

2. Mixed Results

This was the team for our opening game against Allentown at King's Court:

Bantam

Brocken Taggert Purdy Robinson

Fish Brown

Mole Jezz McCann Singh

Subs: Alexiou, Matthews

There was no programme, because the Brontley Building Society publicity department had decided they couldn't afford to keep on doing them for every match. They would do them for cup-ties. We were mad about that. The programmes were good. We could show them to people and it proved we were playing for a big team and not just in some Saturday morning team.

Our team showed three changes from the last game in the Qualifying Competition, all at the back. Robbo Robinson had come off the subs' bench to replace Alex Alexiou, which was more or less expected because we needed his height and strength. Chris Taggert had taken Cyril's place, which nobody had expected, least of all Cyril. And Tony Bantam was back in goal in place of Ally Scott.

'Why is Cyril out and Chris in?' I asked Harpur. 'What do you think?'

'Reckon it's Tom Brocken,' Harpur said. 'He's Captain, and a good player, but he lacks a bit of pace and gets exposed. I think Chris Taggert got in because he can cover for Tom. He has an extra bit of pace that Cyril hasn't. Also Chris is good on high balls, and that will help in the middle.'

It made sense. Harpur is good at thinking things out like that.

It wasn't much of a match in the first half.

Maybe we had all been too keyed up for it, because it was our first game and we thought we had to get off to a cracking start to impress everybody and win the League.

The result was a lot of crash-tackling, particularly from Ronnie Purdy and Chris. They seemed to be in a competition to see who could break someone's leg first.

Chris got a yellow card right at the start for bringing down their winger. Ronnie didn't, but he should have. He kept giving away niggly little fouls. Tommy was up out of the dug-out, yelling at him to calm down.

I didn't see much of the ball early on. Harpur works my side of the field, and he was forced back because the player he was marking was big and strong. The result was that Singhy and I were left stranded, and when we did get the ball forward it tended to go wide on the right, with Joe Fish feeding Danny Mole.

Danny made two or three good runs and got the ball inside, but their central defenders were dominating and Jezzer and I couldn't get on the end of anything.

Lester managed to cut in from the wing and send one header just over the top, when he should have scored. It was a let-off for Allentown, and the usual happened. Just when we were buzzing, their central striker got away on the left and slung over a low cross. Their Number 7 was cutting in, and he met the ball with a diving header.

Goal!

0–1 to Allentown. It was partly down to Tom Brocken, who had been outpaced by the central striker, and partly to Ronnie Purdy, who should have been covering the Number 7. Ronnie was out of position, paying more attention to ball-watching than where his man was, and when he looked round the Allentown player had the ball in our net.

That was the score at half-time.

N. McCann Super Star had hardly touched the ball.

'Make something happen, Napper!' Tommy said to me. 'What are you and Jezzer doing out there? Picking daisies?'

Just after half-time Tommy told Matty Matthews to warm up. Matty was sprinting up and down the line, which meant one of us would be off, and we would revert to Route One stuff, instead of working it down the middle.

Maybe it was a shrewd move on Tommy's part to get us going. I don't know. Anyway, it worked.

We were about ten minutes into the second half when Harpur Brown fed Lester Singh wide on the left.

There didn't seem to be anything on, but Harpur flighted a through ball behind the back and Lester moved on to it at 500 miles an hour. Sometimes when Lester does that he puts his

15

head down and runs into nothing, but this time he looked up, and spotted Jezzer heading for the far post screaming and waving his arms. Lester stopped, came inside the back, who was struggling to catch him, and then, instead of playing what looked like the natural ball to Jezzer, he laid it flat across the box, to me.

WHAM-BAM!

A rocket-blaster Napper Super Goal!

Their keeper never sniffed it! The ball came just where I like it and, with their defenders moving to cover the obvious in-swinger to Jezz, there was no one near me and I just hit it!

This was the position, with Harpur on the ball:

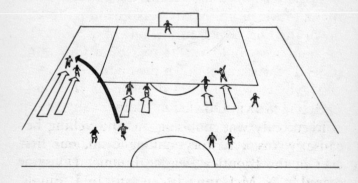

The interesting thing about the goal (apart from the absolutely brilliant Super Star Strike!) was that Lester did what Lester doesn't usually do: he played a simple direct ball that wasn't the obvious one, because for once in his life he had stopped and looked, instead of just hammering in his cross. My marker had moved off me, anticipating that Jezz would get inside the back, which he had, and that left me absolutely open when the ball was slipped square, instead of being drilled into the far post.

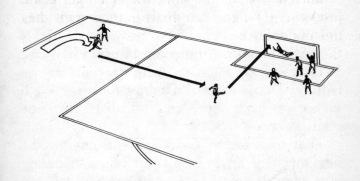

GOAL! GOAL! GOAL!

Everybody was mobbing me and yelling because it was a History-making Goal, our first ever in the Brontley League Premier Division, scored by N. McCann with an assist by L. Singh, and laid on by H. Brown, ex-Red Row Stars, like me, so really it was a Red Row Stars Goal.

We thought we would go on and win the match.

Then Tony Bantam went up for a cross and fell awkwardly.

The ref stopped the game and both trainers came on and the next thing we knew Tony was coming off the pitch with the Allentown trainer holding his arm. It was a broken shoulder, though we didn't know that at the time.

Big Matty came on and went in goal.

Allentown started playing balls down the middle to test him. Matty didn't come off his line, and they got two goals even though they didn't do much else.

1–3. The injury to our Star Keeper had cost us the game.

'OK! Don't worry!' Tommy told us. 'We'll pick it up next week. You did all right. Same team. No problems!'

That meant that Cyril was still out for the next one, which was tough on Cyril, considering how edgy Ronnie Purdy and Chris had been in the centre of our defence.

The one change Tommy *had* to make was Ally Scott coming in for Tony in nets.

'No problem!' Harpur said, and I agreed with him. We were lucky having two keepers who could both be relied on.

'Win the next few, and we'll be on our way!' I said.

It didn't work out that way, although what happened had nothing to do with our defence.

It was the attack that let us down.

Ally did well in the next two games, keeping a clear sheet in the first one against BYC, and only letting in one against Silvertown. The trouble was that we didn't score in either game, so after three games we were third from the bottom, with only Vale United and Queenstown beneath us, although we had the same number of points as Celthill.

This was the bottom-of-the-table League positions after three games . . . and the bottom was where we *didn't* want to be.

		HOME					AWAY					
	P	W	D	L	F	A	W	D	L	F	A	Pts
BYC	3	0	1	0	0	0	0	1	1	1	5	2
Celthill	3	0	0	2	2	5	0	1	0	0	0	1
Warne Colts	3	0	0	1	1	3	0	1	1	0	1	1
Vale United	3	0	0	2	4	5	0	0	1	2	3	0
Queenstown	3	0	0	3	0	7	0	0	0	0	0	0

Scottown and Kings Aston were top with nine points each, undefeated, so we already had to make up an eight-point gap if we were going to make a challenge for the League.

Tommy made changes. Marty Legget came in for Danny Mole on the right wing, because one goal in three matches suggested we had to change something up front. Cyril came in for Chris Taggert at the back, with Chris moving forward to partner Harpur Brown in midfield, replacing Joe Fish, who went on to the bench.

This was the team for our fourth game, against Celthill:

Scott

Brocken Purdy Small Robinson

Taggert Brown

Legget Jezz McCann Singh

Subs: Alexiou, Fish

Warne County Colts 6 – Celthill 0!

I got two, and laid one on for Marty Legget. Lester got one, Harpur got one from a header, and Jezzer got one near the end, just before he had to go off with groin strain.

That let big Matty in for the next game, which was Scottown away. It was tough on Danny Mole, but Tommy wanted to see how we would do with height in the middle, which we hadn't had with Jezzer and myself together.

Matty came in, and scored.

I got three, so I was top scorer, with six goals in five games!

Scottown Albion 1 – Warne County Colts 4!

That was the score in our fifth match. We had seven points and were coming out of the danger zone. It looked as if we might be able to challenge the top teams.

We played our next match against Queenstown.

Queenstown 1 – Warne County Colts 3!

3–1 against Queenstown away wasn't so good because they had a terrible defensive record, but it was still a win. I was pleased Jezzer was back. I didn't play as well feeding off big Matty's knock-downs as I did combining with Jezzer. Even so, Lester scored and so did Marty Legget, twice, but I didn't!

Then Warne County Colts 0 – Kings Aston 2!

It was a bad result for us because so much depended on it. Going into the game Kings Aston had only dropped two points out of a possible eighteen, after drawing with Swans, who were fourth in the table and going well. If we had beaten Kings Aston we would have been on thirteen points after seven games, and only three behind them. But we lost, so they stayed top on nineteen points, and we were nine adrift, stuck in mid-table on ten points, with a third of the League gone.

That was awful enough, but the really awful thing was *why* we lost. It was the same as in our first game, an injured goalie in the second half when we were being outplayed, but still hanging on and hoping to sneak one. Ally came rushing out of his area to drop-kick a loose ball to touch. He was slow off his line, and he met the ball and their striker at the same time.

Crack!

Stretcher. Ambulance.

One goalie with a broken shoulder. One goalie with a broken leg!

Tom Brocken went in goal this time, but he could do nothing about the two that beat him. One was a penalty after Ronnie up-ended somebody in the box. The second was a free when Chris Taggert brought his man down in a last-man position.

Chris was sent off. The ref couldn't do anything else.

Three players out for the next game, and no goalie!

'Don't worry!' Tommy said in the dressing-room, after the game. 'Keep playing your football. The results will come.'

The results hadn't been too bad.

We were on Played 7, Won 3, Drawn 1, Lost 3, Goals For 14, Goals Against 8, Points 10, and we were sixth in the League, although we were trailing the leaders by a long way.

This was our playing record before our League Cup-tie, which was the first break we got from the League battle:

Allentown	(H)	1–3
BYC	(A)	0–0
Silvertown	(A)	0–1
Celthill	(H)	6–0
Scottown	(A)	4–1
Queenstown	(A)	3–1
Kings Aston	(H)	0–2

Bad luck with injuries about summed it up, because we hadn't met anybody yet who was really better than we were.

'So we must have a chance!' I said.

'All we need to do is string a few results together!' Cyril said.

'With no goalie,' Harpur pointed out. 'Our first League Cup-tie coming up, and we don't have anyone to do nets!'

The only consolation was that it was a game

we couldn't lose: versus Bassett in the League Cup. It was the game Marty Legget absolutely wanted to win more than any of the others, because they were his old team.

'We'll walk it!' Cyril said. 'Division Two team? No chance!'

That's what we all thought . . .

WARNE COUNTY COLTS

WARNE COUNTY FC

v.

BASSETT

JACK DADE BRONTLEY LEAGUE CUP

KO 11 a.m.

PRODUCTION OF THIS PROGRAMME SPONSORED BY
THE BRONTLEY BUILDING SOCIETY

TOMMY SAYS...

Played 7, Won 3, Drawn 1, Lost 3, Goals for 14,
Goals against 8, Points 10

Our record in the Brontley League Premier Division this season speaks for itself, and what it says is *inconsistent*. Injuries have played their part in our up-and-down results so far, particularly the double misfortune of losing not one, but *two* outstanding keepers. But on the whole I have been satisfied with the results, particularly the goals-for column. An average of two goals a game suggests that our strikers are on form, and we have found the net on five out of our seven outings.

The team is settling now, although we have dropped points we could have won. With only a third of the season gone we have everything to play for! Today we will be expecting goals from our top striker Napper McCann and his partner Jezzer Jezz (still on the one-goal mark, but hunting for more!), backed up by wingers Lester Singh and Marty Legget (who plays against his old club). At the back I expect Ronnie Purdy and Skipper Tom Brocken to keep things steady. In the absence of Chris Taggert (suspended) midfielder Joe Fish regains his place, and no doubt will be looking to impress.

News of our two injured keepers is mixed. Tony Bantam has come out of plaster, but Ally Scott is still hopping about on crutches. We hope Tony may be fit to resume in the New Year. The question of who-keeps-goal today remains unresolved at the time of writing, but you can be sure that every effort is being made to sign a suitable custodian!

TODAY'S TEAMS

WARNE COUNTY COLTS		Bassett	
(Black & white stripes, black shorts)	v.	(Old gold shirts and shorts)	
Dooley	1	Fleming	1
Brocken	2	Christie	2
Purdy	3	Molu	3
Small	4	Inaya	4
Robinson	5	Snider	5
Fish	6	Metcalf	6
Brown	7	Bunyon	10
Legget	8	Blaney	7
Jezz	9	Junnet	9
McCann	10	Walsh	11
Singh	11	Sloan	8
Alexiou	12	Wolon	12
Mole	14	Magill	14

Match Officials
Ref: H. Thomas. Linesmen: G. Mogore, E. Wyth.

WARNE COUNTY COLTS APPEARANCES AND GOAL-SCORERS:
Bantam 1, Scott 6, Brocken 7, Purdy 7, Small 4, Robinson 7, Fish 3 1s,
Brown 7(1), Taggert 7, Mole 3, Legget 4(3), Jezz 6(1), McCann 7(6),
Matthews 1 1s(1), Singh 7(2), Alexiou 3s

TODAY'S VISITORS

Poor performances in last season's Zaniger League led to Bassett's placing
in Division Two of the new Brontley League, but this season has seen a rapid
revival in their fortunes. They top Division Two, and are at present unbeaten.
Goal-scorers Blaney (8) and Sloan (5) are the stars to watch, and they will
be all out to cause what would surely be one of the shocks of the competition
if successful in overcoming Colts today.

3. Warne County Colts v. Bassett

'Forget the "Division Two" stuff!' Tommy said. 'This team is unbeaten. They had a bad season last year, and so they got dumped into the Second . . . but this isn't the team that did it! New players, a new team, and they've got used to winning. They *expect* to win, and they have got nothing to lose. We are supposed to be Premier Division, two divisions better than they are . . . it makes beating us lovely stuff, as far as they are concerned.'

It was supposed to be a pep talk, but I thought it was just making everybody nervous, especially the new goalie, Kev Dooley. He had turned up and been introduced to everybody in the dressing-room, just before we got stripped, which is a bad start for anybody. He was tall and thin and bony, with legs like matchsticks and bright red hair. He sat with his head down, in the corner, not looking at anybody, and fingering his big goalie gloves nervously.

'Where did they get him?' Joe Fish said to me as we were leaving the dressing-room.

'Don't know,' I said.

This was our line-up:

Dooley
Brocken Purdy Small Robinson
Fish Brown
Legget Jezz McCann Singh

Subs: Alexiou, Mole

So there we were, out on the field facing our first League Cup-tie against an unbeaten team that we were supposed to hammer easily but mightn't, with a keeper none of us had ever met before.

Big Kev didn't stretch himself in the kick-about. Singhy threw him in a few crosses, which he took on his line, but he let go anything that was hit wide of him.

Some keepers are like that. Others don't like to see the ball hit the net at all, even in a kick-in. Kev Dooley obviously wasn't one of them. His handling looked good, so I thought we would be all right on the high balls. Ally Scott had had some trouble with them, and Ronnie Purdy had been giving him stick about it. With Big Kev I thought Ronnie could rest easy.

That is what it looked like when play started.

They came at us straight from the kick-off,

with two wide men making runs at Robbo and
Tom Brocken, and Blaney, their big goal-scorer,
playing down the middle of the park. Tommy
had told Ronnie Purdy to man-to-man Blaney
until the match got settled down, and Ronnie
took up position straight away, breathing down
Blaney's neck.

It turned out to be a mistake.

Blaney didn't play his game in the box. He
turned up there all right, when it counted, but
he came from deep, very fast, making little
chinking runs when he had the ball, and darting
into good positions when he hadn't.

From our point of view it meant that Ronnie was pulled out from the back, tracking Blaney, which left space for their front men to move into. The other catch was that Blaney had Ronnie for speed. Twice he worked his way into clear positions, and twice Ronnie ended up almost clattering him. The first time Blaney broke into the box and fired over the bar. Big Kev was admiring him from the goal-line instead of advancing to cut the angle. The second time Ronnie sent Blaney flying, and got a talking-to from the ref.

That had Tommy up off the bench, yelling to Joe Fish to pick Blaney up in midfield, leaving Ronnie to tuck in at the back and help out Tom Brocken and Robbo with the wide men.

Joe isn't as hard in the tackle as Ronnie is, but he is quick, and he was able to jockey Blaney wide the next time the Number 7 ran at our defence.

Our real problem was going forward. We'd come out expecting them to go at us because we were the favourites and it was a cup-tie and they had nothing to lose. Tommy had said we were to keep it tight for the first ten minutes, and let them run themselves out. Because of that nobody had tried much to go forward, though Singhy had a run and I just failed to connect with his centre. After the first ten minutes, we were supposed to come at them, but pulling Joe back had left Harpur as a one-man midfield, and he was struggling to get any service to our front men.

Tommy saw that was happening and signalled Marty Legget to go deeper, which meant that there was space on the right for Jezzer and me to move into if a break was on. That was fine, but our system depended on playing to each other in close situations, and with one of us pulling wide that left the other one running into their two big centre-backs, Snider and Inaya.

It was case of Bang and Crash.

If the banger didn't get you, the crasher did.

Jezz was the first to run into trouble. I had laid a cross-ball for him just short of the box and he went for it with Inaya. He beat the Number 4's lunging tackle only to run into a bull charge from Snider that sent him flying. We should have had a free kick in a dangerous position but the ref waved play on. Two minutes later, it happened again, but this time Inaya's boot caught Jezzer in the thigh. It was a fifty-fifty ball and the Number 4 didn't mean to foul Jezz, so there was no free kick, but we were getting the message that they were taking no prisoners at the back.

Jezzer was left limping, so he went wide on the right, and I was stuck on my own making runs down the middle.

Marty Legget won the ball just inside our half. He played it across the centre circle to Harpur, who hit it on the volley in behind their right-back, where Singhy was sprinting clear. Singhy got the ball and curled it across, and I went up with the two bulldozers.

Penalty!
Brilliant!
At least, I thought it was brilliant when they'd finished patching up my eye, and I was able to get up!

'You want to take it, Napper?' Tom Brocken asked.

I shook my head. The trouble was I was still feeling wobbly, and the cut above my eye was beginning to swell.

'Give it to me, Tom!' Marty Legget said, running up and grabbing the ball.

It was his old team, so of course he wanted to get on the score-sheet.

Here's an action replay of Marty's penalty:

GOAL!

1–0 to us, twenty minutes gone.

We'd taken their opening ten-minute rush, worked our way back into the game, and now we were on top.

Well, we should have been, but Jezzer was

still limping on the wing, and I was walking around with a lump that felt like a table-tennis ball where Snider had elbowed me. Our attack was all out of joint.

Tommy was yelling at Cyril and Ronnie to push up and help Harpur so that Marty Legget could get forward again.

It backfired on us.

Cyril and Ronnie did press up, but they did it together, and suddenly we were square at the back with Blaney on the ball, after he'd managed to nutmeg Joe Fish. Blaney went between Ronnie and Cyril. He was head-on for the goal, just inside the area, with Big Kev Dooley standing stuck on his line and not advancing.

Blaney shot.

Big Kev had gone the wrong way. He was diving right and the ball was going left but somehow he stuck out one bony leg and hit the ball with his knee. It went up in the air and bounced over the line for a corner, just the wrong side of the post from the Bassett point of view.

Everybody was clapping and cheering Big Kev for a miracle save, but really it wasn't. He'd done well to turn the ball away, but he should never have been caught on his line in the first place.

He didn't seem to know it. He got up looking really pleased with himself.

The corner came across right under the bar and he flipped it over, as if he could do that sort of thing all day, even with Snider crowding up his back.

Second corner, from the other side.

The ball was just like the first one. Tom Brocken yelled, 'Keeper!' and let it go, and Big Kev stood and watched it without moving a muscle. The ball went over his head and banged off the inside of the upright to Ronnie's feet. Ronnie hoofed it back over the line for another corner.

'Your ball,' Big Kev said to Tom.

'Eh?' Tom said.

'I'll call if I'm coming,' Big Kev said.

'In your box, it is your ball!' Tom shouted at him.

'If I don't call, you take it,' Big Kev said.

Tom stood there looking disgusted.

The third corner.

Another in-swinger.

Nobody called and everybody went for it: Tom and Big Kev and Robbo. The result was that Big Kev got his hands to it at the same moment that they hit him. He ended up in the back of the net with the ball, which had screwed out of his hands and come down over the line.

No goal!

The ref gave us a free kick. It must have been against Snider, who'd come barging in, but he hadn't touched Kev. We were lucky that we hadn't given away an own goal.

Kev and Robbo and Tom were all yelling at each other, and Tommy was sitting on the bench with his head in his hands.

Harpur took the free kick.

He did it quickly, while half the Bassett team were still trying to argue with the ref.

Lester Singh got clear on the left, took the ball to the byline, and screwed in a cross to me.

BANG!

Another Napper McCann Super Goal, which put me on seven for the season, three in front of Marty Legget, who was on four after the penalty.

2–0 to us.

That was the way it stayed until half-time.

2–0 seemed all right, considering they had really had more of the play than we had, and they had virtually gifted us the two goals by giving away the penalty, and then arguing with the ref and not covering back for the quick free kick.

'Well spotted, Harpur!' Tommy said, and he praised Lester and me for the way we'd taken advantage of the sudden space at the back. Big Kev and Tom and Robbo were still arguing about the corner, but Tommy didn't waste time on them. He told Kev to get his calls right and then he looked at Jezzer's leg and said he was pulling him off and he told me I was off as well.

'Och, Tommy, I scored!' I said.

'You might need stitches in that eye, son,' he said.

'It's not that kind of cut,' I said, but he wouldn't listen. He put Danny Mole on to play down the middle and told Marty Legget to get back on the wing, bringing Alexiou on to play midfield with Harpur.

It worked.

We got another goal while I was still changing in the dressing-room. It was a Tom Brocken header from a corner, which made it 3–0.

Then Alex got muddled up in calling with Big Kev, and back-passed into the empty net, which made it 3–1. Alex was disgusted, because he had only just come on.

We centred, and the ball went straight upfield to Danny Mole. Snider came at him with Inaya, the tough-guy double-act, but this time Danny barged his way through both of them and stuck the ball hard in the left-hand corner, giving the keeper no chance.

4–1 to us.

That seemed to knock the stuffing out of Bassett. Blaney was wandering around muttering at people, and he'd stopped making his runs, so Joe Fish was able to come off him and do some setting up on our account. Marty Legget was jinking inside and causing all sorts of trouble and Snider and Inaya were a lot quieter, now they were up against someone who could take their tackles in his stride.

Danny got his second, and our fifth, just before the final whistle.

5–1.

'Easy!' Cyril said, when we were down in the dressing-room.

'Those two at the back like dishing it out, but they couldn't take it when Danny came on!' Lester said.

I looked at Jezz and shrugged.

We'd spent most of the Qualifying Tournament proving to people that the team worked best with two small, quick players down the middle, and now Danny Mole had come on and won the game ... well, almost ... by showing that we needed a bit of height and weight to do the job.

'Horses for courses, Napper!' Mr Hope said, when we were going home in his car afterwards. 'They were a good team, but you outplayed them convincingly on the day.'

'We already had the game won when Napper had to go off,' Cyril said. 'No thanks to our goalie, though.'

Mr Hope glanced round at him. 'Big lad,' he said. 'Give him time to play himself in.'

'He was dead lucky,' Cyril said. 'He could have given away three goals, easy, *and* the own goal was down to him, even though it was Alex who copped it.'

Mr Hope said something about Big Kev being unsettled by the defenders shouting at him, and how that was the kind of muddle that would sort itself out when he got used to who-does-what at the back of the defence.

'If he stays in the team long enough!' Cyril said.

'We haven't anybody else, have we?' Mr Hope said. 'Not till Tony Bantam gets back, and that will be a month or two yet.'

'Sooner the better,' Cyril said.

'Can't judge anybody on one game!' Mr Hope said. 'The lad is a good shot-stopper anyway. Remember that one in the first half, just after we scored the first?'

'Yeah,' Cyril said. 'One save!'

'See how it goes!' Mr Hope said.

'We won, anyway!' I said. 'Wonder who we'll get in the next round?'

'Doesn't matter!' Cyril said. 'It's got our name on it!'

That's absolutely typical Cyril. We'd beaten a tough old Second Division team that knew more about kicking than football, and he already had us in the League Cup Final.

4. Going for the Treble

Everything was fine.

We'd won our First Round Jack Dade Brontley League Cup-tie 5–1. That was good going against a team unbeaten up to then, even if they were Second Division.

We won the next three League games on the trot: 3–2 against Carncross, away, 4–3 against Swans at home and 2–1 against Vale. N. McCann Super Star chalked up three more, leaving me top scorer on ten goals. Marty Legget missed the games against Swans and Vale with injury, but he scored two against Carncross, which put him on six, four behind me. Jezzer began scoring at last with one against Carncross and two against Swans, which put him level on three goals with Lester Singh and Danny Mole. Tommy Cowans was very pleased, because our strikers were on song.

The defence wasn't doing so well. Although we won the three League games after the Bassett match, goals were going in against us. Kev Dooley wasn't to blame for most of them, but he didn't give the players in front of him much confidence. He was a good shot-stopper, but very reluctant to come off his line, and Ronnie and Cyril were used to Tony Bantam and Ally Scott coming for everything.

Tommy took Kev for some special sessions with the First Team keeper, and Kev did it brilliantly in practice, but when it came to matches he was still afraid to leave his goal.

'You're big for your age, son,' Tommy told him. 'The box is yours. Anything coming across, you ought to be able to claim it! Make up your mind quickly, let everyone know you are coming, and when you start out of your box make sure you get the ball.'

We still kept losing goals the same way.

Nobody said much, so long as we kept on winning and moving up the table, but everybody was hoping Tony Bantam would get back in as soon as possible.

After ten games we were lying fourth in the league, on nineteen points, and in a strong challenging position.

	P	W	D	L	F	A	Pts
Kings Aston	10	8	2	0	23	8	26
Allentown	10	6	3	1	21	14	21
Silvertown	10	6	3	1	18	11	21
Warne County Colts	10	6	1	3	23	14	19

'In other words,' Tommy told us, 'the three teams that have beaten you are the three teams you have to beat. We could have won all three of those games, and if we had you would be out there in front instead of Kings Aston.'

'If!' Harpur Brown said.

'We'll do them all in the second half of the season!' Cyril said. 'Unbeaten in the last four games! Who'll give me a bet on the double? League and League Cup?'

'Why not make it a treble, Cyril?' I said. 'You think we're going to lose out in the Open Cup, do you?'

'No way!' said Cyril. 'We'll win everything!'

That was before the game against Olympic, which was one we knew we *had* to win if we were to keep pace with the teams above us. We thought it looked hopeful because Silvertown were playing Allentown at home that Saturday. Whatever happened one of them would lose points, and we would come out in a strong position at the halfway mark in our League programme. Our goal difference was better than both of theirs, so if one of them lost we would hop into third spot, behind the team that won their game.

'We must beat these!' Harpur said before the game. He meant we were sure to beat them. They had beaten us in the Western Area

Qualifiers the previous season, but that was before our team was properly sorted out. Now they were eight points behind us in the Premier League, with a few bad defeats, like 1–5 to Allentown and 0–4 to Kings Aston, and a draw with Celthill, who were bottom of the league.

'We beat Celthill 6–0!' Harpur pointed out. 'We ought to walk it against Olympic.'

I wasn't so sure.

I didn't see how a team could go from making all the running in one season to being also-rans the next, which was what seemed to have happened to them.

The answer was clear enough.

Their team that had beaten us in the Qualifying Competition was: Hilley, Once, Hilton, Rolston, Indont, Dooley, Richardson, Straw, Dola, Lamont, Claymore, with Dyall and Taylor as subs.

The team that lined up against us at King's Court for our home fixture in the Brontley Premier Division was: Hilley, Jackson, Dyall, Simpson, Rolston, Indont, Maguire, Grey, Lamont, Cela, Taylor, with Connor and Gallagher as subs.

'Seven new players!' Tom Brocken said.

They'd done well against us the previous season because they were a big team. That meant that because of the age limit a lot of their players had had to be replaced when the new season started. None of our players was over the age limit when the season began, because Tommy hadn't signed anybody to play in the Qualifying Competition who would be and we all had our birth certificates to prove it. The only changes we had from the team that played them before were changes he'd made to strengthen the team.

'Three points in the bag!' Cyril said.

We reckoned their team changes were the important thing. Well, they were, though not in the way we expected. It was a player who wasn't even in the team that made all the difference, but we didn't find that out till long after the final whistle.

The game looked like a cakewalk for us but it wasn't quite as simple as that, even though we were two up at half-time. We had goals from Big Matty, who was in because Lester was injured, and Marty Legget. They came at us in the second half and almost scored early on, but Kev Dooley made a blinding save at the foot of the near post. Then we went upfield and scored another ... N. McCann Super Striker again, my eleventh goal in twelve matches, so I was a goal-a-game striker! Tom Brocken had to go off injured, and Alex came on as sub, and we began to come unstuck. Nobody knew why, but they began to dominate, even though they didn't score.

They *should* have scored, but they didn't.

Big Kev Dooley was the reason they didn't.

First he stopped a rocket shot at the near post.

Then he turned a header from Cela over the bar.

Then, for once in his life, he came off his line when he was supposed to, and took the ball from Cela's feet when it looked odds-on a goal.

Tommy and Mr Hope were cheering him like mad, and the more the game went on, the better he got.

Brilliant saves like that turn a game, and Olympic lost heart towards the end. I got another one – twelve goals in twelve games! – and Alex managed to score, just before the end, making it 5–0 to us.

Silvertown had lost 1–3 to Allentown in a morning kick-off, so we were level with them on points, but above them on goal difference.

Everybody was pleased. Even the Club Chairman, Duncan Murphy, came down to the dressing-room and congratulated us.

Tommy didn't come near the dressing-room until we were all changed. He'd been down to the ref's room with one of the Olympic officials, and when he came in to us he looked really mad.

'Dooley?' he said to Big Kev. 'Out you come. I need a word.'

I've never seen Tommy look so grim.

We didn't know what had happened.

Tommy and Big Kev weren't on the bus that took us back to Owen Lane, and neither was Mr Hope, so Cyril and I had to hang round after the other players had gone off, because Mr Hope usually gives us a lift back home.

We were there until nearly six o'clock, and then Tommy and Mr Hope turned up in the Chairman's car. They all went into the office.

'Just a call or two to make, boys!' Mr Hope said to us. 'I won't keep you long.'

It was almost half six before he came out.

He got us into the car.

Neither of us wanted to be the one who asked first, but Cyril cracked before me.

'What's happened, sir?' he asked Mr Hope. Mr Hope used to be our headmaster at Red Row, and that's why we call him sir. It is a habit that's difficult to get out of.

'Disaster! Disaster! Disaster!' Mr Hope said. He's always had the habit of repeating himself (Cyril used to do a great imitation of him). This time he sounded so serious that we never even thought of grinning.

'What sort of disaster?' Cyril asked anxiously.

'Big Kev Dooley is over the age limit for the competition!' he said. 'He isn't Kev Dooley at all. His name is *Dave* Dooley, but he used his brother Kevin's birth certificate to fool everyone, so that he could sign for us.'

'That's why he's bigger than everybody else!' I said.

'Got it in one, Napper!' Mr Hope said. 'He *looked* big for his age, but he said he was all right and we said, "Show us your birth certificate then." He did and we said, "Great. Sign for us, son, and you are in the team Saturday, because both our keepers are injured." Then he ran out of luck. Olympic had a player called Chris Dooley last time we played them. He is over age, which is why he isn't in their team now. And he has a cousin called Kev, who was supposed to be in our team. Chris was surprised because he knows his cousin Kev isn't much of a footballer, but he came along out of interest. To cut a long story short, when our team came out, there was a Dooley in it, but it wasn't cousin Kev. It was cousin Dave.'

We sat there taking it in.

'What will happen?' I asked.

'That's up to the League Committee,' Mr Hope said. 'But you can be pretty sure of one thing. We won't be playing Silvertown in the next round of the League Cup, and Bassett will be.'

'But we beat Bassett!' Cyril said.

'We fielded an over-age player!' Mr Hope said. 'That means they get awarded the match.'

It was just my luck again, getting myself stuck in a team that had an over-age player.

Present: J. Dade, Chairman (Queenstown)
F. Archer (Neton Heath)
K. Rice (Allentown)
M. Smith (Ormysby)
D. Owens (Vale)
H. Metcalfe, Hon. Secretary (Elm Villa)

The Chairman stated that the purpose of the Special Meeting was to deal with problems arising from the fielding of an unregistered player by Warne County Colts in a League fixture against Olympic YC.

In compliance with Rule 14b Olympic YC, in the person of their secretary H. Goodbody, had formally protested.

The alleged circumstances were that D. Dooley, an unregistered player, had taken part in the fixture, in contravention of Rule 14b.

The player was entered on the team-sheet submitted to referee K. Lines under the name of K. Dooley, a properly registered player.

Subsequent to the fixture being played the referee had been approached by officials of Olympic YC and a spectator, who alleged that the player shown on the team-sheet had not taken part in the fixture, and an ineligible player had been fielded in his place.

After consultation with T. Cowans, Manager of the Warne County Colts, and the player concerned, the complaint was substantiated.

In a submission to the Committee Mr Cowans of Warne County Colts stated that D. Dooley had misled the Club to the extent of submitting the birth certificate of a relative to accompany his registration form. He further stated that D. Dooley had taken part in three League fixtures, those against Carncross, Swans and Vale, and in a League Cup-tie against Bassett. Warne County Colts acknowledged that they were unwittingly in breach of Rule 14b regarding the fielding of ineligible players and apologized to the Committee. He hoped that the Disciplinary Committee would accept that the Club had been wilfully misled by the player, and that it had never been their intention to deceive.

Following Mr Cowans' submission on behalf of Warne County, the Chairman stated that he was sure he spoke for everyone in accepting the assurance that the Warne County Club had acted in good faith. This was agreed by all present.

Mr Cowans thanked the Committee, and then withdrew to allow the Committee to deliberate on their findings.

The findings of the Committee were as follows:

1. In permitting an unregistered player to field, Warne County were in clear breach of Rule 14b in the League Handbook, which covered all fixtures played under the auspices of the League.

2. The Committee accepted that the Club were acting in good faith in fielding the player, having been intentionally misled as to his identity.

3. Notwithstanding the above finding, it was the duty of the Disciplinary Committee to enforce the Rules of the Competition as laid down in the League Handbook.

4. The Committee recognized that the offence was of a technical nature, and were anxious to facilitate the Club, but the interests of others in the competition who were not in breach of the rules had to take precedence. The Committee were concerned at the number of games which had been involved before the offence came to light, and the effect this might have on League Positions of other clubs.

5. Accordingly the Committee ruled as follows:

a) With regard to the League Cup competition Warne County Colts were in clear breach of Rule 14b and were therefore dismissed from the competition. Their fixture with Bassett was deemed forfeit, and therefore Bassett would proceed to the next round of the competition. Both clubs to be notified accordingly.

b) With regard to the four League fixtures in question it was agreed that a cash penalty as allowed for in Rule 14b was not appropriate, as the Club had acted in good faith when registering the player.

Several members felt that Warne County Colts should forfeit the League points won to the clubs concerned, viz. Carncross, Swans, Vale, and Olympic YC.

However, a clear feeling emerged in discussion that adopting this procedure could distort the Final League Table, giving unfair advantage to some clubs involved in League Title or Relegation positions.

It was proposed that Warne County Colts should forfeit the points for the games in question, without points being awarded to the other teams involved, although this also gave rise to some unfairness.

It was alternatively proposed that all Warne County Colts' League fixtures for the season should be declared void, and that the Club should complete their programme of League fixtures on a friendly basis. In this way neither League Title nor Relegation issues would be affected.

A third proposal was that the games be replayed at a later stage in the season, although not all members were agreed on the practicality of this.

The Committee were unable to reach agreement on any of these proposals, and the Chairman therefore ruled that the matter be deferred to an Emergency Meeting of the Full Executive, to be arranged.

H. Metcalfe
(Honorary Secretary)

WARNE-D OFF!

Warne County Colts have been suspended from further League games in the Brontley Premier League following an Emergency Meeting of the League's Full Committee.

The effect of this ruling is that Warne will be demoted from the League's Premier Division at the end of this season, and will compete in the First Division next year.

Warne have also been dismissed from the Brontley League Cup (Jack Dade Trophy) Competition, but will be permitted to play in the Open Cup Competition.

A spokesman for the League expressed regret at the need for the suspension in the light of the fact that Warne County had acted in good faith throughout, having been deliberately misled by the player concerned. There was, however, no other decision the League could make, taking into consideration the interests of all the other clubs, particularly those concerned with League Title or Relegation issues.

Club officials were unavailable for comment last night.

5. Chucked Out!

That was it!

We were suspended from the League and the League Cup, relegated to the First Division, and left with only a series of rotten friendlies to play in . . . if the Club decided to keep the Colts team going at all.

I thought it would be just my luck if they didn't, but they did!

We had a big meeting before the First Team's home match on the Saturday, when we should have been playing Allentown in the League. We thought we would be playing them in a friendly instead, but when Tommy contacted their manager he said that they preferred not to fulfil the fixture, in the circumstances.

'What circumstances?' I asked Mr Hope when he told us.

'I think they voted against us at the meeting,' Mr Hope said. 'Maybe they were right. I don't know. It just seems an extraordinarily harsh punishment for a very minor offence!'

'I bet Allentown and Silvertown and Kings

Aston wanted us out!' Cyril said. 'They thought we were going to win it, so they voted against us.'

'Nobody voted against us, Cyril,' Mr Hope said.

'You just said Allentown did!' Cyril said.

'Allentown raised the point about unfairness to the other clubs,' Mr Hope said. 'They weren't voting against us, they were trying to make sure that no one got an unfair advantage over anyone else.'

'We could have replayed the games!' Cyril said. He was red in the face, and really upset. We all were. It seemed absolutely and totally unfair that we could be out of everything . . . well, almost everything . . . when we hadn't been aware of breaking their silly rules.

'That's the way it is, Cyril!' Mr Hope said.

We felt miserable standing round in the yard at Owen Lane and watching the people go in for the First Team game. We were waiting for Tommy to come out to us. Ronnie was going round muttering about what he would do to Dooley if he caught him and Cyril was moaning about it not being fair. We were all down in the dumps because it looked as if our season was over.

Tommy came out.

'Come on!' he said. 'Everybody inside. Big meeting in the boardroom, so we can sort out our problems.'

'Some chance!' Ronnie said.

Tommy took us in and we saw the trophies and the old Warne County team pictures. He told us to sit down round the boardroom table where the directors sit. He sat at the top of the table with Mr Hope as Chief Scout beside him, and he started to talk.

'Warne County Colts aren't finished!' he said. 'This season isn't over yet! The League are within their rights in suspending us, and there isn't much more we can do on that score, though George Trotman and our Chairman are considering taking the matter higher . . . but even if they do, the season will be almost over before it gets sorted out. But one thing is clear to everyone involved in the management of this club: we are all agreed that you lads ought to be kept together. So that is question one settled. There *will* be a team for you to play for!'

'Who against?' Ronnie Purdy grunted.

'Most of the teams will be happy to fill the blank in their fixtures left by our suspension by playing us in friendlies,' Tommy said.

'Not all of them!' muttered Ronnie.

'That's a matter for the clubs concerned,' Tommy said. 'The bottom line is that the rules were made to keep the Competition fair, and we broke them.'

'You can't get more unfair than by chucking us out!' Ronnie Purdy said. 'I didn't know this

League was got up to stop kids playing foot-ball!'

Somebody cheered! That's what we all thought.

'You will get to play,' Tommy said patiently. 'Where the League teams don't give us a game, we'll find you some other opposition most weeks, and then there's the Open Cup. We can still play in that, and I think it leaves us with something to prove to the others, doesn't it?'

He paused.

'What are we going to do in the Cup?' he said.

'Win it!' Cyril shouted.

'Be nice, wouldn't it?' Tommy said. 'That's what we are going to do. This team isn't going to lie down and die just because people have ganged up on us and we've fallen foul of the rules! The Open Cup is all that is left for us this season, so from now on that is what we're training for and working at. We're going to build a team that can win the Cup!'

'Yo! Yo! Yo!' Cyril shouted.

He was bouncing about.

No one else was . . .

Because we were Warne County's Youth Squad, we'd got special seats along the touch-line in front of the main stand for the First Team game, and we all trooped off to watch it.

It wasn't a bad game, though the ref was playing in the other team's jersey, but I couldn't keep my mind on it. We'd all been banking on having a good season in the Brontley Premier, doing well in the League and maybe winning it, and now we had no games to do well in and we were already relegated.

It was difficult to watch County out there, instead of being out there ourselves, as we had been every other Saturday in the season. It was different of course, because of the crowd and everything, but we still felt part of County. We were their third team, almost, although really none of us would have been old enough to play for the Firsts . . . but all of us thought we *might* have got on if somebody broke an ankle in the kick-in and the subs had to be used and we were short of a sub, something like that. We were signed players after all. I think we were, anyway. I'm not sure if our signing only counted for the Youth Squad. Tony Bantam had played one game for County Reserves when their keeper cried off at the last moment, so I suppose we could have been recruited, though it wasn't very likely.

I sat there watching the match and thinking that my football career had come to a great big zero. It would be a waste of time unless we got a run in the Open Cup. We should have been mixed up in the fight for the title, and now we were down to friendlies, and just the one competition.

Warne County won, so that cheered me up a bit, but I was right about the friendlies. They were rotten, because we needed proper matches that mattered, and friendlies aren't like that.

Tommy switched things about a bit, experimenting with the side now that points didn't matter, and there were good things. Two new players for a start. Dennis Lake was one. He turned out to be a sound keeper, though not as good as Tony. The other one was called Bill

Coller and he was signed to give us more strength in the middle, and allow Harpur more time to get forward.

That was the plus side.

The minus was that Danny Mole was injured and was out for weeks, and Singhy got fed up and started not coming down to training. We were lopsided without him, so Marty Legget switched to the left, with Jezzer still in the middle but covering the right, which meant that I was left in the central striking role!

Lots of N. McCann Super Wham Bam Goals.

Four in eight games, but none of them really counted, because they weren't proper games. There were no League points at stake.

'Watch it, Napper!' Tommy said to me. 'The edge is going off your game.'

Then he had me on the subs' bench for a week or two, with Matty going down the middle, but I got back in the week before the First Round of the Cup. I think he did it to give me a warning, and get me right on my game for the Big One.

The Big, Big, Big Thing was the Cup Draw, and it worked out Big, Big, Bigger than anybody expected!

BRONTLEY OPEN CUP, First Round: Warne County Colts v. Allentown.

Brilliant!

They'd got us suspended from the League, and then they had chickened out of meeting us in a friendly straight afterwards.

Now they were going to get what was coming to them!

WARNE COUNTY COLTS

v.

ALLENTOWN
BRONTLEY LEAGUE OPEN CUP
KO 3 p.m.

PRODUCTION OF THIS PROGRAMME SPONSORED BY
THE BRONTLEY BUILDING SOCIETY

TOMMY SAYS...

Despite our off-the-field difficulties I am more than satisfied with the team's progress. One consequence of the lack of competitive games in the run-up to this competition is that I have been able to experiment with different systems of play. It has been noticeable in the last few weeks that our defence has tightened following the inclusion of Bill Coller in the centre midfield.This has allowed more scope for Harpur Brown and Joe Fish and/or Chris Taggert to get forward and combine with 'Napper' and 'Jezz'. Both strikers are well in form. Our goalkeeping problems have been eased by the signing of Dennis Lake, who has performed well in his appearances to date. Despite the enforced restriction on competitive matches, our lads are shaping well.

TODAY'S TEAMS		
WARNE COUNTY COLTS (Black & white stripes, black shorts)	v.	**Allentown** (Blue shirts, blue shorts)
Lake	1	Hempsey *1*
Brocken	2	Golder *2*
Purdy	3	Marks *3*
Small	4	Wyn *6*
Robinson	5	Hamilton *11*
Taggert *Fish*	6	Smith *7*
~~Coller~~	7	Grey *5 8*
Brown	8	Dornan
McCann	9	Chamberlain *9*
Jezz	10	Lynch *10*
Legget	11	Croasset *4*
~~Fish~~ *Alex*	12	Smiley *12*
Matthews	14	Forset *14*

Match Officials
Ref: H. Thomas. Linesmen: D. Scott, H. Maguire.

TODAY'S VISITORS
Allentown are very welcome visitors today. Their League form to date has been consistent, if not striking, and they lie midway in the Premier Division table, with twenty-six points. 'Dosh' Chamberlain and Micky Croasset combine to provide a high-scoring front line but, in recent weeks, following injuries to key players, the defence has leaked six goals in the League, and four in their elimination from the League Cup Quarter-finals by leaders Kings Aston. Everything points to a high-scoring encounter between two teams whose remaining chance of a trophy this season is at stake.

6. Grudge Match

It was the match we *had* to win, against the team we reckoned had got us put out of the League, but right from the start everything was against us!

'We can't play on that!' Harpur gasped when he saw the pitch.

It was more like a mud-sea than a pitch, and the rain was belting down. The kind of pitch that doesn't suit a play-the-ball-about team like ours, with players like Harpur, me, Marty Legget and Jezzer. Proper football didn't seem possible. I thought Tommy might change the team, and bring Matty off the subs' bench to start the match, because he is big and could plough through it.

Tommy didn't.

Tommy had other troubles on his mind.

We were down in the dressing-room huddled round the gas heater when the ref came in. We thought it was about calling the match off, because of the conditions. But it wasn't. He was holding our team-sheet.

He called Tommy over to the corner.

We couldn't hear what he said, but Tommy nearly went up the wall! His face went white with anger, and he stood there jabbing his finger at the team-sheet. Then he rushed out of the room saying, 'This is ridiculous!'

Duncan Murphy, our Chairman, came back with Tommy and the ref. Duncan Murphy is a well-known headcase. He had been going round saying he was going to take the League to the FA and stuff like that, and this time he really blew his top.

The ref let him go on and on, and then stopped him right at the end, and read him a lecture. Duncan Murphy turned on his heel and walked out shouting something about you'll-hear-more-of-this, and about it being a fix.

Tommy had been standing there thinking. He started talking to the ref. The ref was being patient, explaining things very carefully to Tommy, and in the end Tommy shook his hand and the ref went out.

Then Tommy called Bill Coller out of the room.

'Not another over-age player!' Tom Brocken muttered. We thought that must be it.

Mr Hope came in and told us to get stripped.

'I think you're in!' he said to Alex. 'Bill Coller is out. Joe Fish goes into midfield in his place, and you make the subs' bench.'

Joe and Alex looked well pleased. Nobody else did.

'Why?' Ronnie Purdy asked. 'Why change the team now, just before the game?'

'Don't ask me!' Mr Hope said. 'Some muck-up about the registration forms.'

That was it. The delay meant that we didn't even have a team talk.

We went out on the pitch with the rain belting down and the mud sucking at our boots.

This was the line-up for what was really the most important game we'd had all season ... because if we didn't win it there would be no season left!

Lake

Brocken Purdy Small Robinson

Taggert Fish Brown

Jezz McCann Legget

Subs: Alexiou, Matthews

'Remember, this lot helped Silvertown to get us chucked out of the League!' Ronnie Purdy said when we were lining up.

'Yeah!' Cyril said, rolling up his sleeves.

They kicked off, and their striker, Dosh Chamberlain, got away. Cyril crash-tackled him over the touch-line and almost into the fence, spraying water all over the place!

Then Chris Taggert bowled over their Number 7 just outside our box, and gave away a silly free kick. They wasted it by trying to play a clever-clever short-pass sequence, and found the ball sticking in the mud.

Next Ronnie Purdy walked all over Dosh. It was the second time the striker had been taken out, and all in the first five minutes.

Robbo wanted to get in on the rough-house act, and he bundled the Number 11 off the ball. It wasn't a tackle, more of a jump-in. The ref blew his whistle and read Robbo a long lecture.

Tommy was up off the bench, yelling at everybody to calm down and play football.

Playing football was the one thing we *couldn't* do, not on that pitch. Most of the time our backs and midfielders were running around crashing into their forwards, to show them what we thought of them, but when they did get the ball and tried to play it forward, the ball just stuck in the mud every time.

'Play it wide! Play it wide!' Tommy shouted.

The trouble with that was that we had a natural right-winger, Marty Legget, playing wide on the left because Lester Singh had dropped out, and our right flank was supposed to be composed of Jezz holding the ball and Tom Brocken overlapping. Tom tried it twice, and each time he ended up flapping in a puddle with the ball on its way back upfield, leaving us exposed. Tom's overlaps had been working for us on hard pitches, which is what we'd had over Christmas, but this wasn't a pitch at all. It was more like a swimming-pool with mud dumped in it. Tom is big and hefty and he couldn't keep his feet, so nothing at all was coming from the right. He was playing like a dinosaur in wellies.

The other problem was that Allentown had improved since the last time we had played them. Then they had won 1–3, in our first game, but that was mainly because of the injury to Tony Bantam which meant he had to go off when the game was 1–1 and we looked like getting on top. Since then they'd brought in Dosh Chamberlain to give them a bit of power up front, and two bigger lads at the back, but the main difference was that they had been playing competitive matches every week, and we had been out of it, keeping going with doesn't-matter-to-the-other-team friendlies. We'd gone slack, and they were on their game.

'Football! Football! Football!' Mr Hope yelled from the line, but it seemed to me about the silliest thing anyone could yell. All we could do was knuckle down and scrimmage for the ball every time it got stuck in a pool . . . it was that kind of game, not a football match.

I think it would have been a bad-tempered one even if we hadn't gone out there knowing that Allentown had helped vote us out of the League. As it was, people like Ronnie and Cyril and Robbo weren't going to let them forget it. With the ball sticking in the mud and the ref's whistle blowing every two minutes the game was more a mud fight than a football match.

'Blow this business!' Jezzer said to me when he had been dumped on his back for the third time. He was covered in mud and taking a lot of stick because their backs had seen what was happening to Dosh and Co. up front, and decided they'd better dish a bit out themselves.

Jezzer drifted out to the right.

It didn't matter much anyway, because Tom Brocken had stopped even trying to get forward, so Jezzer wasn't taking his space.

Tom had problems of his own.

His flank was the muddiest of the lot, but their Number 4, Croasset, must have had extra studs or something. He was waltzing round Tom and firing the ball across, cleverly mixing high balls and pull-backs. Dennis Lake came off his line again and again, taking everything, but sooner or later we knew they would get something from it.

It was sooner.

Croasset jinked Tom, got to the line, and put a high ball over. Dennis was back-pedalling,

going for a catch, when the Number 7 came
running in, not offering much of a challenge.
Then Dennis slipped, and sprawled on his back.
The ball sailed across the goal, hit the inside of
the post, and came out right at the Number 7's
feet.

He prodded it into the net.

1–0 to Allentown.

They deserved it, even though it was a soft
old goal.

Then for once I got clear.

I wouldn't have, but their big centre-back
lost the ball in a puddle and I was on it like a
flash, into the area, round the goalie, heading
too far wide, and I poked the ball towards the
goal.

Goal! Goal! Goal!

Another Napper McCann Cracker.

But it wasn't.

It stuck on the line! Just my luck again!

I ended up sliding off the pitch on the seat of
my shorts while their Number 3 got back and
played the ball out of danger, showering himself
in dirty water in the process.

It *was* a goal, every way but the way that
counted.

The only chance that I'd got to do anything
right through the half and I'd got it right,
everything right, and still the ball wouldn't go in
the net.

Straight down the other end, and Ronnie Purdy forgot all about the ball and took Dosh Chamberlain out in our box.

Penalty. He was lucky not to be sent off, although it wasn't a last-man tackle. I suppose the ref gave him the benefit of the doubt because of the conditions, but I would have sent him off, because he *meant* to get the man.

Dennis Lake saved it.

Dosh took the kick himself, and Dennis threw himself up and sideways and somehow tipped the ball over the bar. It was a well-taken kick and Dosh deserved to score, but even he couldn't help clapping Dennis.

The corner came to nothing, and then the half-time whistle went.

0–1 down, and looking like losers.

Tommy *roared* at us in the dressing-room, particularly at Ronnie.

'You're playing like a headcase!' he told Ronnie. 'Away and get your shower. You're off, son!'

Ronnie swore at him.

'What's that, son?' Tommy said, whirling round.

'It isn't my fault. We're playing like puddings and the pitch is a pudding!' Ronnie said.

'On your way!' Tommy said. 'I'm taking you off for your own good, because if I don't you'll be sent off!'

72

'That's OK!' Ronnie said. 'If you don't want me in your team, that's good enough for me!'

He slung his things off and went into the shower, slamming the door behind him.

'See that?' Tommy said. 'That's the trouble with this team! That's big-mouthing, not football. You can beat this lot if you play a bit, but we'll get nowhere if you go out there and try to kick them off the park.'

Then he stalked out.

'What's got up Tommy's nose?' Harpur muttered to me.

Mr Hope heard him, though he wasn't supposed to. He had been standing round looking glum while Tommy lost his temper.

'I'll tell you what's wrong!' he said. 'You aren't trying to play football. You're turning this into a grudge match, where you have to teach the other team a lesson for something they're supposed to have done. The result is that tempers are flying all round, and you've forgotten to play football.'

Ronnie chose that moment to come out of the shower.

'Especially our Ronnie!' Mr Hope said.

Ronnie went bright red. Mr Hope was right. Ronnie had been stoking us up for it, going round muttering about how we would teach Allentown a lesson.

Then we had to go out again, back on to the field.

It was a day when we needed a proper team talk, and there wasn't time to have it. It was OK telling us to play football, but how were we to do it on a mud-patch in the pelting rain?

Tom Brocken was good. He told Marty Legget to switch back to his old position on the right, and Jezzer to go wide on the left. Chris Taggert was to play up front and use his strength through the middle with me, switching back to the old four-two-four formation, but playing it a different way.

'We'll play on the bits of the pitch where we *can* play football,' Tom said. 'Keep it on the dry land!'

Tom's idea was simple. The middle of the field was a marsh, so the link-ups that should have been happening between Jezz and me with Harpur or Joe Fish coming through were all breaking down, stuck in the mud.

'Long balls down the wing to the wide men,' Tom said. 'No messing about. Get it in the box where Chris can fight for it, and hope that Napper manages to get on the end of something for a change. And keep the ball out of the centre circle!'

It began to work.

Marty Legget, back on his best side, started going round the left back. Marty was skating past him in a cloud of spray from the puddles. Their left-winger pulled back when he saw that

Marty was beating his man, and that gave Tom Brocken the chance to come forward himself. Marty was going to the line and slinging crosses over. When the ball stuck in the mud it was in the middle of their penalty area, close to goal, at the end of the move, instead of in the centre circle at the beginning of the move, which was what had been happening in the first half. With the ball skidding about and sticking in the mud in that area, something was bound to go right. That's what we hoped, anyway.

We set up a siege on their goal in the first ten minutes, banging the ball in low from the right. The left was a lost cause because the ground out there was like a lagoon. Jezzer saw that it was and moved inside . . . that's what he said anyway, but I think he was hoping he would sneak something out of the morass in front of goal.

He nearly did.

A cross came over and Chris went for it with the keeper. They both missed it and Jezzer came sliding in at the far post to knock it home. He screwed it wide with the goal empty.

Then another ball broke loose in the area after Chris mistimed a header and it fell to me.

I only had a second to see it but I cracked it and it looked like another N. McCann Super Screamer into the top corner, but the goalie got up and tipped it over.

The corner came across from Joe Fish, who is good with the dead-ball stuff. Tom Brocken got on the end of it and crashed the ball against the bar with the keeper nowhere. It came down and one of their backs swung his leg at it and missed, and I came sliding in and pinged it against a post, when I had the whole net to aim at.

Another let-off for them.

Still 0–1 down.

Their manager was up on the line, yelling at his team. Then he sent on a big lad called Smiley, and put him wide on their left, to help cut off the supply.

It worked.

Both teams had worked out that the ball was going nowhere on one side of the park because of the state of the swamp, and both teams kept going the other way, our right wing, their left. We had exploited it first, but their manager bottled it up with his substitution.

We were still on top.

Their keeper saved three in a row. One from me and one from Harpur, who hit in a long drive that skidded off the mud and almost beat him. The third was when he came out and dived in a puddle at Chris Taggert's feet.

Chris should have beaten the keeper to it, but he looked like what he was – a defender shoved up front to fight his way through the mud. He hadn't the pace or the goal-instinct to get on the end of it.

Then they got away down the left, splashing the ball through the swamp. The winger put his cross over and Dosh Chamberlain came in and nodded as neat a goal as you could see, far down in the corner, where Dennis Lake couldn't reach it.

0–2.

Out of the Cup!

Out of everything, really. That is what it looked like.

Tommy was up from the bench, with Big Matty beside him, waving Cyril Small's number.

Cyril off, Matty on.

Matty went to centre-forward, and Chris went to the back. I think he was glad.

I didn't know what to think. We were right back to the old formation Warne Colts used to play before Jezzer and I got established as the strikers. Jezzer and I play it nippy, running off each other. Matty's game is to plough down the middle after everything, bouncing off defenders and causing problems.

'Any knock-downs, stick them away!' he said to us.

It is not the way we like to play, but it was probably the best thing to do in the circum-stances, when we were two down in a cup-tie on a pitch that made real football impossible.

We were hoping that the tactical substitution would work, and make the game swing in our favour.

Well, it swung all right, but what happened had nothing to do with tactic or substitutions, and a lot to do with adapting to the conditions. On a bad pitch, chase everything is the rule!

Twenty minutes to go. We were piling forward with nothing going for us. They were looking as if they might get one on the break and really stitch us up when their right-back tried a back pass from twenty metres outside the box.

On a good day, it would have been nothing.

On *this* bad day, the ball stuck in the mud at the edge of the area.

I got on to it, all on my own, following up just in case.

The keeper came dashing out. I side-stepped him and I tapped the ball into the empty net!

1–2!

The back picked the keeper up. They both looked really cheesed off. The back could have played the ball into touch, or even risked a turn, but a back pass is just what you *don't* do on a pitch that looks more like a swamp than anything else.

Then Jezzer was brought down outside the area.

Normally, Harpur takes frees in that sort of

position. He can place the ball, and we have a whole routine of frees, some of them going back to the days when we played for Red Row, but this time Tom Brocken grabbed the ball.

Tom can hit the ball all right. The problem is that he is more likely to hit the corner flag with it than the net.

Usually!

Not this time!

WHAM!

2–2!

We were back in it.

Three minutes later there was another scrimmage, when their keeper dropped the greasy ball.

It hit their left-back, who swung at it, trying to put it away for a corner. He mishit it, and the ball spun up over the keeper.

Guess who got on the end of it!

N. McCann Super Star of the Universe had smashed another one.

3–2!

We were all over them.

Right at the end Tom broke through in the middle . . . how he got there nobody knows . . . and the back scythed him down.

Penalty.

'Hat trick, Napper?' Tom said, handing me the ball.

BANG!

Another N. McCann Super Goal!

4–2 to us.

That is how it finished.

Dennis Lake was just a spectatator for the last twenty minutes. He didn't mind. He came off shivering with cold but grinning all over his face.

'Your penalty save could have turned it!' Tom said to him, and I think he was right.

We had w-o-n! We were through to the next round. That was all that mattered. Keeping going despite the pitch, chasing everything even when nothing seemed on, had won us the game.

Afterwards Tommy came into the dressing-room with somebody we didn't know.

'See this man?' he said, pointing to the stranger. 'You know who this is?'

'Yeah,' Tom Brocken said, but he didn't sound very friendly.

'This is Mr Rice,' Tommy said. 'George Rice. Chairman of Allentown. Know what he did today?'

'Yeah!' somebody said. 'Came along to see us knocked out of the Cup, same as he got us chucked out of the League.'

'Got it *wrong*, haven't you?' Tommy said.

Silence.

'This man kept us *in* the Cup, when we *should* have been out of it, by rights!'

Cyril said, 'I thought it was Napper got the hat trick!'

'You know what we had today? Another signing mix-up, that's what!' Tommy said. 'This man sorted it out. He stopped us putting out a team that would have had us chucked out of the competition. We would have been out, *his* team would have gone through. I want you to thank this man. Come on, say it!'

'Thanks, Mr Rice,' everybody said, though we didn't understand it then.

What had happened was really screwy. It

was K. Dooley all over again!

We had sixteen players, then we signed a player calling himself K. Dooley. We got chucked out of the League because he was really D. Dooley, and he was over age. That was bad, but it should have been the end of it. Then we signed Dennis Lake to cover the keeper problem, and Bill Coller, which brought us up to eighteen players, which is the maximum number allowed under the League Regulations.

That is what everybody thought – Tommy, Mr Hope, and all the team . . . eighteen players.

The problem was that K. Dooley was *still* signed on. The real K. Dooley *could* have played for us, except that he is some kind of computer genius who has never played football in his life.

So with the real K. Dooley still on our books, Dennis Lake was the eighteenth player, and Bill Coller was number nineteen . . . and we weren't allowed nineteen players under the rules. It *would* have been spotted when we sent our team-sheets in, but because we only played friendlies there were no team-sheets to send.

Mr Rice of Allentown had kept us in the Cup, when we could have been chucked out. Instead, his team were out. Maybe he was trying to make up for getting us chucked out of the League.

'We'll draw Queenstown in the next round,' Harpur said. 'That would be good. Their Chairman is the League Chairman, and we could show him how wrong the League was!'

'We'd thrash them!' Cyril said. 'County's name is on the Open Cup!'

We were all thinking that, really, but all we could do was wait and see who we got in the draw.

'If it isn't Queenstown, I hope it is Kings Aston or Silvertown!' Cyril said. 'I want to beat the biggest teams in it to show them we would have won the League if the others hadn't cheated and got us chucked out.'

Cyril likes saying things like that, but the truth was that we were the ones who had cheated, even if we didn't mean to. The other clubs had tried to sort things out in a way that would be fair to everybody. It was just our tough luck that it came out badly for us.

The more people went on about it being unfair and how we would get our own back, the more likely we were to come unstuck.

What we needed was a lucky draw in the next round against a soft side, to give us time to get the team sorted out. We'd beaten Allentown on persistence, and adapting our game to the circumstances. The result had everything to do with that, and very little to do with football.

'But being able to adapt to the conditions *is* part of football!' Mr Hope said, when we were talking about it afterwards.

That seemed to make sense!

OPEN CUP DRAW

The draw for the second Round of the Brontley League Open Cup resulted as follows:

Celthill v. Romsey
Bassett v. Kings Aston
Olympic YC v. Vale
Barnsdale v. Warne County Colts
Hume v. Silvertown
BYC v. Scottown
Elm Villa v. Queenstown
Swinley Town Colts v. Swans

Top matches of the round should be at Hume, who encounter old rivals Silvertown from the Premier Division, and Elm Park, where Villa, First Division Suprise Packets in the League Cup, try to prove that their victory over Silvertown in that competition was no fluke by tackling Premier Division Queenstown. Romsey of the Second Division will be hoping to upset Premier bottom team Celthill. Bassett appear to have little chance against all-conquering Kings Aston, whilst Warne County Colts, Vale and Swans will expect to go through. The tie between BYC and Scottown is probably too close to call! All in all an intriguing draw, where most of the League's 'Big Fish' have managed to avoid each other.

MATCH PROGRAMME
Brontley League Open Cup

KO: 2 p.m.

Teams:

BARNSDALE	v.	Warne County Colts
Dorley	1	
Skinner	2	
Marks	3	
Crisp	4	
Woley	5	Details Not
Sawer	6	Available
Quinn	7	
Maskey	8	
Lynch	9	
Bassett	10	
Kincaid	11	
Walters	12	
Smith	14	

Match Officials:
Ref: J. Wunn. Linesmen: H. Washly, S. Longue

TODAY'S MATCH
We welcome Premier Division opposition today in Warne County Colts, and the young 'Barneys' will be out to prove themselves as Giantkillers! Whatever the result, I am sure our lads will not be overawed by the opposition, and will give a good account of themselves.

B. Jones (Manager)

7. Lucky?

It was a lucky draw! A Second Division team who weren't going anywhere. That's what we thought. People were saying we'd been lucky to get Allentown on a mud-pitch, and now we were lucky again.

'You make your own luck in football!' Tommy said. 'Let the other teams worry about it!'

This is the team Tommy fielded for our Second Round Tie in the Open Cup against Barnsdale:

Lake
Brocken Taggert Small Robinson
Fish Brown
Legget Jezz McCann Singh

Subs: Purdy, Matthews

It didn't appear in the scruffy bit of paper they issued as a programme though, because they never bothered to ask us for a team list in advance. Ronnie Purdy reckoned they were ripping off Building Society Programme Sponsorship money. I put it in my programme collection, though really it was no good.

The good news they could have printed in their programme, if they had bothered to ask, was that Lester Singh was back on the left, which allowed Marty Legget to switch back to the right, his natural side. I don't know what happened about Lester. He just turned up at training again, looking sheepish, but I was glad to have him back in the team. Probably he heard we had a Cup Run going and didn't want to miss out. Tommy picked him anyway, so they must have sorted out whatever the row between them was.

The bad news was Ronnie Purdy. Tommy was very annoyed with him. He said Ronnie had gone into the match against Allentown with the idea of roughing people up, and Tommy wasn't going to have that in his team. I think it was meant to be a message to Cyril and Robbo as well, because they had all got it into their heads that Allentown deserved all they got.

'You started the match as if you wanted to kick them off the park,' Tommy said. 'Result? Two goals down by half-time. In the second half you changed round, played some football and won! Makes sense to me!'

What he didn't say was that that was all

down to Tom Brocken, who'd made the switches that changed everything in the second half. They were changes that Tommy should have made himself, if he hadn't lost his temper and walked out of the dressing-room.

I thought Ronnie might have quit after the row. But he didn't.

'We'll miss him at the back,' Cyril said doubtfully.

It seemed a big risk, when we were up against a team of Second Division cloggers, who might try to kick us off the park if they couldn't match us for skill.

'We're supposed to be the skill team!' Harpur pointed out. 'That's why Jezz and Napper are down the middle instead of Danny Mole and Matty.' He didn't say it, but it was also why he was in the team, and Cyril was in and out of it. Cyril is a good stopper, but Harpur can make things happen.

'If you can't play creatively at this level, you never will,' Tommy told us. 'We're going to win this match on skill!'

'Bet we get another mud-patch!' Cyril said.

We didn't.

We got an ice-rink instead, with the pitch frozen and slippy and only just playable.

'They'll crash into us and kill us!' Joe Fish said when we looked at Barnsdale out on the pitch. They were *all* big, I mean B-I-G big, and they set off as if they were going to run us off the park, in a Giantkilling act.

They tried to, as well. But it didn't work!

The rock-hard pitch was made for us, because Jezzer and I and Marty Legget all have good control, and we were quicker on the turn than their big defenders. Harpur and Joe were linking up with us and going on runs and the big Barnsdale bruisers went around tackling the air.

The first ten minutes was about the only time they were in it.

Their idea of tactics was to throw the ball high into the box, behind our defenders, and try to take Dennis Lake out when he came to clear it. The very first ball Dennis came for, their centre took him hard. Dennis ended up on the ground with the ball and their striker ended up in the book.

Three minutes later, they did it again. The same high ball, hoofed up the middle so that it cleared Cyril, dropping just short of our box. Dennis had read it, and he came out to head clear, and got a boot on the shoulder for his pains from a forward who hadn't any hope of the ball.

Another booking!

Mr Hope had to come on to help Dennis back on his feet, and Tommy was up from the bench yelling at Cyril and Robbo to give the keeper some cover.

The trouble is that you can do that for fair challenges, shielding the keeper till he has the ball, but you have to rely on the ref when forwards go in late on a keeper in possession.

That is just what happened.

Robbo had played a short ball back into the box when he was under pressure, and Dennis came to collect it. It was safe enough, no problem, but this is what happened.

The good news was that the player who tried to do Dennis was given the red card.

The bad news was that Cyril was sent off with him, for fighting!

Ten men apiece, and we thought that it might play into their hands by upsetting the balance of our team, but it didn't. With only twenty players on the field, there was a lot more space, and we used it.

Once . . .

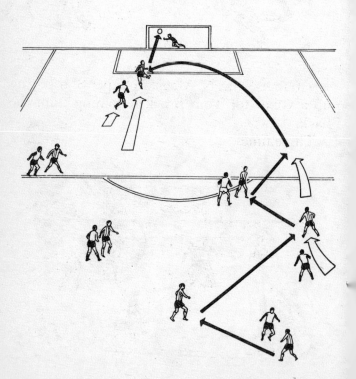

1–0 to us, with Jezzer on the end of it.
Twice . . .

2–0 to us, with N. McCann Super Star setting
up a volley for Tom Brocken coming from the
back.
Three times . . .

3–0.

That was it.

Game over.

Then I got one, and Lester Singh made it five with a solo run.

5–0 at half-time.

Tommy jumped on Lester as soon as we got into the dressing-room, saying he should have squared the ball across, because Jezzer and I were free. It was tough on Lester, who had waltzed it round three men and the keeper and walked it into the net, but I think Tommy was right.

Here is Lester's goal:

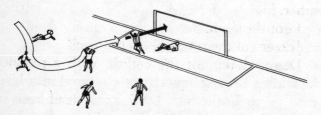

And here is what he should have done:

'We want you to be brilliant, son,' Tommy told Lester. 'But not at the expense of the team. You start doing pretty bits, like your last goal. You get Kings Aston or Silvertown in the next round, and you won't waltz round their defenders. OK, you scored. But it was a bad goal. We didn't score it, they gave it to us.'

'Bad habits! Bad habits! Bad habits!' said Mr Hope, shaking his head.

Scoring goals seems to me like a good habit, but I knew what he was getting at.

The second half was all pretty patterns, with people side-passing when they were clear of the defence trying to set up tap-in chances for each other.

I got the sixth.

Jezzer got the seventh, his hat trick.

Dennis Lake got the eighth, with a penalty kick after Chris Taggert was clattered in a last-man tackle in the box. Dennis was dead keen to get on the score-sheet (most goalies are) and we let him come up and take it because it didn't matter. He almost blew the net away.

The defender who had gone for Chris was off, and they were down to nine men.

It didn't make much difference.

Just one more goal, a header from Tom Brocken when they missed out on marking his run at a corner kick.

9–0!

Everybody was glad when the whistle went.

Matches like that are no good to anyone.

'You lucky lot!' their keeper said to me coming off the field.

'Eh?' I said.

'Wrong pitch for us, wasn't it?' he said. 'If we'd got a soft ground that suited us we'd have done you! You can't play our kind of football on an ice-rink.'

I didn't bother to answer. We weren't lucky. We had a team that could adapt to the conditions, that's all. I suppose the keeper had to say something after 9–0!

'Still . . . we're in the Quarter-finals!' Cyril said.

'*We* are, son, *you're* not!' Tommy said.

He was right of course. Being sent off meant Cyril was automatically out of our Quarter-final tie, because he had to miss the next competitive match, and we hadn't got any competitive matches except the Cup.

'Lesson one, Cyril! Leave it to the ref!' Mr Hope said. 'A nothing team, a nothing game, and you got yourself sent off when the ref had it under control anyway! You could have cost us the match if things had worked out differently.'

I felt sorry for Cyril, but we were all too excited to worry much.

Mr Hope came into the dressing-room with all the Second Round results.

Celthill 2 Romsey 2
Bassett 0 Kings Aston 6
Olympic YC 0 Vale 2
Barnsdale 0 Warne County Colts 9
Hume 1 Silvertown 2
BYC 3 Scottown 1
Elm Villa 6 Queenstown 2
Swinley Town Colts 0 Swans 2

'We're Top Hot-shots!' Cyril bawled. '9–0! That will show them.'

'Yes,' Tom Brocken said. 'But look at Elm Villa. Playing a team a division above them, and they win 6–2! They're in the Semis of the League Cup as well. They must be good even if they are only a Division One team.'

'I reckon something went wrong on the day,' I said. 'Queenstown are doing well now in the Premier Division. They don't go round losing like that. Maybe it was an ice-pitch, like ours.'

'Who do you fancy playing, Napper?' Harpur said.

'Silvertown!' I said. 'Or one of the Premier teams. I'm fed up with being told how lucky we are. Silvertown or Kings Aston. They are the top teams in it, and we'll have to meet them sooner or later, if we are going to win it. Beat one of them, and nobody can say we are lucky.'

'Right!' Harpur said. 'We need a tough draw!'

And we got it!

OPEN CUP DRAW

The draw for the Quarter-finals of the Brontley League Open Cup resulted as follows:

Vale v. Silvertown
Warne County Colts v. Kings Aston
Elm Villa v. Romsey
Swans v. BYC

Tie of the round pairs Premier Division rivals Vale and Silvertown. Vale have impressed in recent weeks, while Silvertown still have an outside hope of a League/Open Cup double.

Kings Aston, runaway leaders of the Premier Division and finalists in the League Cup, should prove too strong for the Warne County Colts, despite the Colts nine-goal demolition of lowly opponents in the second round ... a game marred by more of the referee trouble Colts seem to take with them wherever they go.

The Giantkillers of the the season, First Division Elm Villa, down to contest the League Cup Final with Kings Aston, should be in little danger from Second Division Romsey, though Romsey's dismissal of Celthill in a replay will have done wonders for their confidence.

Swans and BYC both languish in mid-table in the Premier Division, and will be relying on a run in the Open Cup to make something of the season. Forecast: BYC ... but it may need a replay.

WARNE COUNTY COLTS

WARNE
COUNTY
FC

v.

KINGS ASTON

BRONTLEY LEAGUE OPEN CUP

KO 3 p.m.

PRODUCTION OF THIS PROGRAMME SPONSORED BY
THE BRONTLEY BUILDING SOCIETY

TOMMY SAYS...

There is nothing like a Cup competition to bring out the best in players, young or old. The 9–0 thrashing of Barnsdale in the last round (McCann 2, Jezz 3, Brocken 2, Singh 1...and goalie(!) Dennis Lake from a penalty were our scorers) was fully justified on the run of play (in fact we should have had more), but was by no means the best we can do. Conditions, plus the standard of the opposition, spoiled this game, marred by several sendings-off. The Colts are aware that I am very concerned with the present disciplinary record of the side, *not* a problem I would have anticipated, but one we all have to face up to. I am sure that today's game will mark an improvement. With the exception of goalie Ally Scott, I now have a full panel of players fit for selection, which is a very pleasant situation for any manager.

TODAY'S TEAMS

WARNE COUNTY COLTS (Black & white stripes, black shorts)	v.	Kings Aston (Red shirts, red shorts)	
Lake	1	Molin	*1*
Brocken	2	Risk	*12*
Taggert	3	Lo	*3*
Robinson	4	Milk	*2*
Alexiou	5	Samms	*4*
Fish	6	Watson (D.)	*6*
Brown	7	Watson (K.)	*9*
Legget	8	Atue	*7*
McCann	9	Dowie	*8*
Jezz	10	King	*10*
Singh	11	Lewis	*11*
Mole	12	~~McKinn~~ *Long!*	*14*
Purdy	13	Stitt	*5*

Match Officials
Ref: K. Hamilton. Linesmen: C. Hothman, G. Darnlie

TODAY'S VISITORS

A glimpse at Kings Aston's record tells it all. They are undefeated after seventeen games in the League, with only two draws (Silvertown and Vale, both away from home), and have reached the final of the League Cup (Jack Dade Trophy) where they must be odds-on to defeat First Division Elm Villa. The Watsons, Kenny and David, have been prominent in midfield all season, with Atue, Risk and King impressive up front, although they will miss injured ace-striker Long in today's tie. Only nine goals conceded in all matches speaks for itself! Today's game should be a real Giantkilling test for the Colts...they don't come any bigger than Kings Aston.

8. The Crunch

The crunch...Kings Aston in the Cup Quarter-finals. We were all convinced that if we beat them we could beat anybody else. They were the top team in the Premier Division, and hadn't been beaten all season. Beat them, and nobody could say we were a lucky team.

'You've got to win it!' Cyril said. 'Win it for me!'

He was bouncing round the dressing-room making a nuisance of himself when he was supposed to be helping. Everybody was there – even Ally Scott came hopping down on his crutches – and everybody was nervous.

'Nothing to worry about!' Tommy said. 'They are unbeaten. They think they've come here to walk all over you. That's great. They don't know what you can do. I do. Remember the last time we played them? Ally Scott does, don't you, Ally?'

'Yeah!' Ally said, patting his crutch.

'They beat us 2–0 down at their place,' Tommy said. 'But their goals came in the second half, with Tom Brocken in goal. First half, when we had a goalie, we could have been in front. So they aren't any better than we are. They just *think* they are . . . and that's working for us. OK?'

'Yeah, boss,' Tom said.

'What we don't do this time, is what you did against Allentown, understand? If you want to prove something, prove it by playing football, not kicking people. I'm fed to the teeth with having incidents, and people sent off and suspended. It isn't going to be that way today. We are going to prove we can beat this team with football . . . so go out and do it!'

Then we went out.

This was the team line-up:

Lake
Brocken Taggert Robinson Alexiou
Fish Brown
Legget Jezz McCann Singh

Subs: Mole, Purdy

Cyril was suspended, and we thought Ronnie would be in, but Tommy had taken a gamble on Alex instead. Goalkeeper must have been a tricky decision. Tony was probably the best in the League before he was injured, but Tommy had stuck with Dennis Lake, who had been getting better with each game, and had never let us down. Tony Bantam had played one friendly after coming back from injury, but I suppose Tommy couldn't be sure about him, and didn't want to risk it.

Alex getting in was different. Tommy had moved Robbo into the middle of the back four to replace Cyril, and slotted Alex in the left-back spot.

'What for? Tommy must be crazy!' Cyril said, when he heard the team.

'Alex is a better footballer than Ronnie,' Harpur pointed out. 'Anyway, Ronnie's been throwing his weight about all season. We have a hard enough game on without risking having a central defender sent off.'

He gave Cyril a look, but Cyril didn't pick it up. The last central defender we'd had sent off was Cyril, and that was what Harpur was getting at.

'We need bite at the back!' Cyril said. I think he was thinking about himself. Ronnie is probably a better player than Cyril, and if Ronnie couldn't get into the side Cyril must have thought his chances were limited.

'Tommy is very keen to win this one with football,' Harpur said. 'That's where Alex comes in.'

I thought that was it. Alex was pleased, but he looked nervous going out, which wasn't prising. He'd been in and out of the team all season, and Ronnie had been playing regularly, so Alex knew Tommy was taking a gamble playing him.

'The same as playing us up the middle, instead of Danny Mole and Matty,' Jezzer said to me.

'Yeah,' I said.

It would be great to win that way ... if it worked.

Kings Aston had only two changes from the team that had beaten us at the start of the season. One was Long, their chief goal-scorer, who was on the subs' bench with a heavily strapped knee. Dowie was on in Long's place. The other was the goalie, Molin, whom we hadn't seen before. He had only played twice before, and was in because of injury.

'As usual, test him early,' Tommy said, and we were all set up to do it.

That meant doing what Barnsdale had tried to do to Dennis Lake ... slinging the ball in so that it fell in no man's land, behind the defenders, but just in front of the goalie's box.

Here's what I mean:

If the backs haven't confidence in the keeper, they go for it, and anything can happen. If the keeper hasn't confidence in the backs he may come for balls he can't get. Either way it puts pressure on early before the keeper has had a proper feel of the ball. When you know the other team has an inexperienced keeper it is the absolutely obvious thing to do.

The worst thing that can happen from a forward's point of view is this:

Or this:

That's what happened.

Two good balls in the first five minutes, and their supposed-to-be-suspect reserve keeper called well and collected both of them. The second one was better for them than the first, because it showed the back had confidence in the keeper. He could have played safe and gone for a corner, but he knew where the keeper would be, and headed it back to him.

Instead of unnerving the keeper, we'd given him two confidence-building touches.

They did the same thing, and Dennis Lake did just as well, so both manoeuvres cancelled each other out. Nobody was going to get any advantage from slinging the ball in to tempt the keeper into a mistake. It is always worth a try early on though, because if it works at the beginning the defence will be at sixes and sevens for the rest of the game.

It was that kind of game.

They were expecting us to run at them, because we were supposed to be the Giantkillers, but Tommy had told us not to do that. He and Mr Hope had been to watch them play, and the interesting thing was that their favourite move was the quick break from the back using Lewis and Stitt. They were both fast wide players, with Long in the middle. Tommy said Kings Aston liked to pull teams on to them, and then play quick stuff on the break.

With Long out, we didn't know what way they would play, but the drill was that Alex would man-mark Stitt and Tom Brocken would do the same to Lewis. Chris Taggert and Robbo would play a kind of double-sweeper till we saw how things worked out.

'If we don't run at them, what do we do, boss?' Tom Brocken asked, sounding exasperated.

'Hold the back to begin with. Don't get over-committed going forward early on,' Tommy said. 'That's the idea . . . but after that you'll have to switch it about according to how the play goes.'

They seemed to have had just the same instruction, and so the first fifteen minutes were all nervous stuff, with nobody risking anything.

There were only two breaks, once when Lester Singh got clear and blazed the ball into the crowd instead of crossing, and on their side when Tom Brocken made a mistake. Tom was last man and he'd lost control of a ball outside our box. Stitt was closing him down, so Tom tapped it over the line for a throw.

Their Number 9, Kenny Watson, grabbed the ball and threw it quickly into the box to his brother, David. David Watson spun past Robbo's lunge-tackle and fired a great shot in that cannoned off the foot of the post and went for a goal-kick.

Tommy was up out of the dug-out, yelling at Tom Brocken.

Tom waved a hand in acknowledgement. It was a really silly mistake. When it comes to a last-man clearance, you have to land it in the crowd, because a quick throw to a team moving up against a split defence can lead to all sorts of trouble. It looks unsporting to boot the ball away when you don't have to, but it isn't. There is a real footballing reason for it, which is to delay the throw until the defenders get back. Tommy told us we had to stop the other side getting a quick throw-in, and the safe way to do it is to give the ball a welt.

Picking it up and tossing it to the opposition can do the same thing – delay the throw – but you can get booked for time-wasting, and you can't get booked for booting it over the stand . . . unless you boot it after the ball has gone out of play, which is asking for a booking.

'Play a bit, Napper!' Mr Hope yelled at me from the side, so I tried going at their central defenders, cross-passing with Jezzer. We had three goes at it that almost came off, and as a result they switched a man deeper, and that took care of it. They had been playing 4–3–3, which gave them three men on our two in the middle. Dropping their Number 4, Samms, into a deeper position meant we were back to two men apiece in midfield.

They got away down the left, the two Watsons again, and their centre-forward Dowie got in a shot from the edge of the box. Dennis Lake did well to tip it over the bar.

Here he is doing it:

With their deep man, the risk of offside was narrowed for us, and Harpur spotted his opportunity, and put Singhy through.

Singhy went level with the box, and switched it back to Harpur, who had come roaring up from behind. Harpur played it one touch behind the last man and into my path.

It would have been another McCann Super Goal if their stand-in goalie hadn't been on top form. We had stand-in goalies at both ends, and both of them were playing as if they were Top Stars!

Dennis made two more saves before half-time, once when he scooped the ball off Kenny Watson's head, and the second time when he punched clear a dangerous header from the left.

Jezzer had a shot easily saved at the far end, but neither team was able to get an advantage.

o–o at half-time.

In we went.

Tommy clapped everybody on the back and looked really pleased.

'This team has scored forty and conceded thirteen all season!' he said. 'That's how well you are playing! They've got the jitters! You're on top!'

'Tell that to Dennis!' Tony Bantam muttered. He was handing me my cup of tea at the time.

'Eh?' I said.

'Kept us in it, he has!' Tony said. I suppose he was looking at it from a goalie's point of view, but maybe he was right. I had pulled one brilliant save out of their keeper, but Dennis must have made half a dozen down our end. Tony was talking about the player who was keeping *him* out of the team, so I don't think he would have said it if he hadn't meant it.

'One goal will do it, lads!' Tommy was saying. 'One goal!'

Then he did something we hadn't expected.

'Substitution!' he announced. 'Ronnie on, Alex off. OK, Alex?'

Alex looked disgusted, but he shrugged and turned away. Ronnie was grinning all over his face.

'Ronnie?' Tommy said. 'Not your usual

game, right? No crash-tackles at the back. You are going walkies.'

'Eh?' Ronnie said.

'Kenny Watson,' Tommy said, 'the big fair-headed lad. Everything is coming through him. We thought Stitt would be playing wide, but instead, with Long on the bench, Stitt has come inside and disappeared. Kenny Watson has been breaking into the wide space, and coming at Alex from deep. I want you to move up from the back and close-mark him.'

Then he told Robbo to be ready to go wide on the left if they switched somebody out there to overlap Watson, which is what he thought they might do when they saw Ronnie man-marking him.

We had a shock when the teams came out because Kenny Watson was missing, and their Number 12, Risk, had come on in his place. So much for Ronnie's marking job.

'What happened to Kenny?' I asked the Number 3, who had been marking me.

'Been bad all week with the flu,' he said. 'We had to pull him off! Just our luck!'

'If he plays like that with flu, I wouldn't like to be up against him when he's fit,' I said.

'Yeah!' the Number 3 said.

We kicked off, and went on to the attack.

Harpur got the ball, and flighted it into the area. It looked like an easy catch for the big keeper, and he came out to take it.

Here's what happened:

G-o-a-l!

Ronnie had stuck the ball in with his very first touch. It should have been me, but I was so surprised when the keeper dropped it that I missed.

Ronnie ran over to the line and did a samba dance for Tommy's benefit. He was lucky the ref didn't book him.

It was amazing. We'd tested the stand-in keeper right from the start with a lot of good balls, between him and the backs, and he'd taken everything. Now Harpur had played a bad ball in, easy pickings, and the goalie made a muck of it!

1—0 to us. The absolute Top Team in the whole League, undefeated in the League and favourites for the League/League Cup/Open Cup treble, and we were beating them in the Open Cup Quarter-final, when they thought they only had to turn up to win it.

They went mad.

I suppose they weren't used to being behind, but suddenly they were all powering forward, anxious to get at us. The manager was up off the bench, yelling at them to calm down, but they weren't listening. It suited us, because they were rushing it, when they might have done better playing their usual game. People were pinging the ball in at Dennis from everywhere, and Dennis was taking everything.

First he saved from the Number 5, Stitt, and then he did it again from a volley by Atue that he turned over the bar. Then Risk broke clear and Dennis took it from his feet. Then Dave Watson hit one from twenty metres out. It took a deflection off Robbo, but Dennis still managed to get a hand to it.

Everybody had gone back, and Tommy was up on the line shouting and yelling at us to push up.

So I pushed up.

I was the only one who did.

It was like one of the Red Row matches again. The Red Row Stars had a tough time, but one thing we used to do was to leave me up where Harpur could find me with a long ball.

I was hoping that would happen again, but it didn't.

It didn't, because nobody at the back could get the ball to feed it forward, not even Harpur. It was all one-way traffic to our goal.

Robbo got back to head over, with Dennis beaten.

Ronnie and Risk got in a tussle on the edge of the box, and Ronnie brought the sub down. Their whole team was yelling for a penalty but the ref didn't give it, and in the end he booked Dave Watson for yelling at him.

Then they made a second sub.

It was Long, their top scorer, with his bad knee. According to the programme, he wasn't fit to play. The manager must have decided to risk him as sub. We soon found out why he was top scorer.

Ronnie went on to him, but three times the big striker just brushed him aside. Panic stations.

The first time Dennis saved Long's shot, the second time he hit the post and their Number 7 put it wide, and the third time Long got the ball in the net but the ref gave him offside when he wasn't.

Long started yelling at the ref and he was booked as well.

Then they got a corner on the right.
Stitt, the Number 5, went over to take it.
It was the usual near-corner routine, like this:

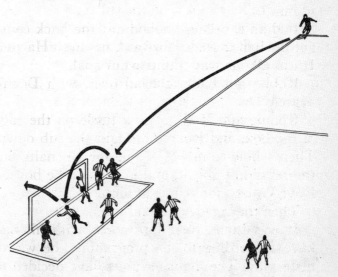

Robbo went to mark the near-post corner, with Ronnie shadowing Long at the back, because we thought he was the danger.

The ball came over, and Robbo went up with Dave Watson, who was trying to flick on.

Watson beat him, and the ball went across the face of the goal, clear over Dennis's head. Ronnie got to it, and put it behind for another corner.

Their manager was up off the bench, clapping his hands.

Same routine, same result, but this time Dennis got a hand to the ball after it flicked off Watson's head, and it broke to the penalty spot, where Risk took it on the volley.

Dennis Lake was still in mid-air from his save, but he managed to twist in mid-air and get an arm up, and the power of Risk's close-range blast took it over the bar.

Here is Dennis making his Wonder Save:

Everybody clapped him, even their manager. It was a Great Stupendous Super Save, the sort of save that matches turn on.

Then we saw that Long was lying in the

penalty area, clutching his leg.

The ref waved his arms and the trainer came on, and the next thing we knew Long was being carried off between Mr Hope and their trainer. His knee had gone again.

They were down to ten men, with their Star Striker off, but we still couldn't get into it.

They kept running at us, but running was the word. They were supposed to be the best footballing team in the Premier Division, but it was all kick and rush.

Tommy put Danny Mole on to stiffen up the midfield, and he yelled at me to go back and waved Singhy in from the wing to the centre. We knew Singhy could run, and we knew he couldn't tackle for butter-nuts, and I suppose Tommy hoped we might get something from it.

We nearly did, and N. McCann Super Star Defender and Goal-maker set it up.

I'd taken the ball off Risk, just outside our area, and I flighted it forward, right over the head of Lo, the Number 3, who had been marking me. Singhy got on to it and put his head down and headed for their goal.

The keeper came right out of his box and Singhy steered it past him. The keeper stuck out his leg and lifted Singhy.

The ref blew his whistle, and ran up, pulling out the red card.

The keeper was sent off. It was a deliberate

last-man foul, and there was nothing else the ref could do.

Samms went in goal, and they were down to nine men, with ten minutes to go.

'Calm it!' Tommy yelled from the line. 'Play it about!'

We couldn't *get* it to play it about.

Tom Brocken tried a blaster against Samms with the free, and almost hit the corner flag, and from the goal-kick they swarmed up the pitch.

Stitt hit the post.

Robbo cleared off the line and hit Ronnie coming in, and Dennis just managed to drop on the ball to stop an own goal.

Then I got back and scooped one off Risk's foot as he was about to bang the equalizer.

The corner came over. Stitt headed on. Dave Watson, coming up at the back, headed against the bar and the ball went for a goal-kick. The whistle blew.

The *final* whistle.

We'd won it!

We'd beaten the best team in the competition and we were through to the Semifinals.

Everybody was mobbing Ronnie and Dennis Lake, and Mr Hope and Tommy and Cyril and Tony Bantam were doing a war-dance on the touch-line.

Nobody noticed their nine men walking off.

'You lucky, lucky sods!' Dave Watson said to me.

'Our name is on the Cup!' Cyril was shouting.

'Nine men, and we were all over you!' Dave Watson said, shaking his head. 'Your keeper saved you! Wait till you have to play Silvertown. You can't get that lucky twice!'

Maybe we *were* lucky, a bit. But we'd gone in front when they still had eleven men on the field, and they were the ones who'd lost their cool and gone charging into attack. If they'd stuck to their game and not panicked they might have beaten us. The combination of a bad substition and having their keeper sent off had cost them the game. Kenny Watson's flu was luck, for us, but then they shouldn't have risked him in the first place. Going into a Cup Quarter-final with *two* dodgy players who didn't last the match was bad management, not bad luck! We'd had players missing too, but we had others who could come in and do the job for us. That is good management, not good luck.

They never thought they were in any danger of losing, and when they did go behind they hadn't the brains to play themselves out of it.

Out of it is just where they deserved to be!

We were through to the Semis, and whether there was luck in it or not didn't seem to matter!

SEMIFINAL DRAW

Elm Villa v. BYC (at Leyland)
Warne County Colts v. Silvertown (at Vale)

The draw for the Semifinals of the Brontley League Open Cup seems to clear the way for a Cup double by Elm Villa, of the League's First Division.

Elm's thrilling 1–1 draw with Kings Aston in the League Cup Final (replay Saturday week at Hume) leaves a Cup double still on. Now they have been paired with BYC, somewhat rugged conquerors of Swans after two Quarter-final replays and a penalty shoot-out finish. Unbeaten all season, Elm Villa must be strongly fancied to defeat their Premier Division opponents, who have little to boast about on their form this season.

If luck wins trophies, Warne County Colts must feel they have their final place booked! Handsomely outplayed by Kings Aston, Tommy Cowan's boys scraped home against an understrength side. They may well find Silvertown carry too much fire-power up front for them this time. Warne County Colts have done enough to show they could win if their remarkable luck holds, but this time the draw has not been kind to them and the odds must be on a Silvertown versus Elm Villa Final ... which is surely what all neutral fans will be hoping for.

Meanwhile, Kings Aston's recent dip in form leaves them with the prospect of losing out in all three competitions. The Premier Division title could well be decided when they meet Silvertown in a virtual Premier Division play-off in three weeks' time. On recent form the Silvers could be in line for a Premier League/Open Cup double, leaving Kings Aston with only the League Cup to show for their efforts this season ... and Elm Villa may have something to say about that, judging by their performance in the drawn game, where they were unlucky not to take the trophy at the first time of asking.

WARNE COUNTY COLTS

v.

SILVERTOWN

BRONTLEY LEAGUE
OPEN CUP SEMIFINAL
KO 3 p.m.

PRODUCTION OF THIS PROGRAMME SPONSORED BY
THE BRONTLEY BUILDING SOCIETY

WELCOME TO THE BRONTLEY LEAGUE OPEN CUP SEMIFINAL

Today's clash at the Vale Stadium brings together two fine young sides in what will undoubtedly prove to be a close contest. Both clubs are to be heartily congratulated on their achievement in reaching the penultimate stage of the Open Cup Competition.

I would like, on behalf of the League, to draw attention yet again to the generosity of our Sponsors, the Brontley Building Society, without whom there would be no Brontley League, and to thank them yet again, on *our* behalf as the League Executive Committee, on behalf of the lads who have gained so much from the games played under their auspices, and on *your* behalf, as spectators.

I am sure that we all look forward to a sporting contest today. May the best team win.

H. Metcalfe (Hon. Secretary)

TODAY'S TEAMS

WARNE COUNTY COLTS: From: Lake, Bantam, Purdy, Mole, Brocken, Small, Alexiou, Fish, Robinson, Taggert, Brown, Jezz, McCann, Matthews, Singh, Legget.

SILVERTOWN: From: Bailey, Webb, Langley, Skinner, Aslon, Cripps, Magee, Swinson, Oates, McCarthy, Watson, Jacks, Acres, Downs, Hale, Bell, Jull.

Queenstown will field in white shirts and blue shorts.
Warne County will field in black and white stripes, black shorts.

Todays Officials are Mr J. Edmond (Monk Norton), referee; K. Clements (Wingfield), red flag and J. Fox (Barnleck), yellow flag.

HOW THEY GOT TO THE SEMIFINAL:

WARNE COUNTY COLTS

Allentown	4–2	McCann 3, Brocken
Barnsdale	9–0	Jezz 3, Brocken 2, McCann 2, Singh, Lake (pen.)
Kings Aston	1–0	Purdy

SILVERTOWN

Carncross	5–1	Bell 2, Hale, Swinson, Oates
Hume	2–1	Hale 2
Vale	4–0	Jull 2, Hale, Webb

9. Sure Shot

'This is it!' Tommy said. 'Cup Semifinal. Win it and you are heroes, lose it and you are forgotten. Same for both teams.'

'We beat Kings Aston. We can beat anybody!' Cyril said.

'That's one sure way of losing this one!' Tommy said, and he showed us the League table.

	P	W	D	L	F	A	Pts
Kings Aston	18	14	3	1	49	17	45
Silvertown	17	13	3	1	29	11	42
Scottown	19	14	1	4	32	18	43

'You beat Kings Aston!' Tommy said. 'Brilliant ... but the Kings Aston team you beat had a sub goalie who let in a soft one, and were down to nine men. Allentown beat them the next week in the League as well. Then Elm Villa drew 1–1 with them in the League Cup Final, even when the Kings had a full squad fit and ready to play again. Elm Villa aren't even in the Premier Division! I'm not interested in Kings Aston. We are not playing them. We are playing Silvertown! They've only lost once in the League, they are three points behind the Kings, with a game in hand . . . and they aren't going to put half-fit players out against us. They won't be reduced to nine men at the finish.'

'And they're on a League/Open Cup double if Kings Aston slip up again!' Tom Brocken said.

'Right!' said Tommy. 'So this isn't a push-over. You are up against it!'

'I don't call that a pep talk!' Cyril said, when we were going out.

I wasn't sure. When we'd beaten Kings Aston, everybody thought our name was on the Cup. I suppose Tommy felt he had to gee us up.

The team Tommy picked was:

Lake
Brocken Small Purdy Mole
Fish Brown
Legget Jezz McCann Singh
Subs: Matthews, Alexiou

It wasn't the team he wanted to pick, but he hadn't much choice about it. First Chris Taggert came out in spots all over, and then Robbo had to pull out with a bad knee. So much for our famous luck! Cyril coming in for Chris was obvious, and Ronnie came back to partner him in the middle. Tommy didn't think playing Alex at the back had worked in the Quarter-final, so he decided to stick Danny Mole in instead. Nobody was sure about that, but Danny is big and strong and Tommy had been working on him in defensive positions. The Squad System, and having players like Danny and Alex who could fit in in most positions, meant that we didn't have the problems Kings Aston had had against us.

'Trouble is, we never know whether we'll be in or out of the team!' Alex said, and I think Danny felt the same way. If they'd been one-position merchants like Singhy or Harpur they'd have been in every week, but because they could fit in most places they tended to be the ones who didn't get a chance to get established and they suffered for it.

'It's being in the squad that is important!' Mr Hope told him.

'It's the Cup,' Danny said. 'You don't get medals for being in the squad.'

'You've still got more chance than a one-position player like Matty, or Tony Bantam,' I said. 'They're either in the team, or they're out.'

Anyway, this time Alex was out, and Danny was in.

It was partly because of the way Silvertown played that Tommy had gone for Danny Mole at left back. They liked the high ball to the far post, and both their wingers were strong on coming in to meet it in the air. Tommy wanted height at the back to counter them. With Tom Brocken and Danny Mole, he reckoned he'd got it.

'Two big backs, but both slow!' Joe Fish said to me. 'Harpur and I will spend all our time covering for them, so that Cyril and Ronnie don't get drawn out of the middle.'

That was one problem. The other was Lester Singh.

'I'm not sure that a non-tackling streak of lightning is a luxury we can afford,' Harpur said to me. 'If Lester doesn't do his stuff, it is like playing Silvertown with ten men.'

'He can't do it if you don't lay it on for him,' I said.

'How can I lay it on for him if I'm back doing the job he should be doing, covering for slowcoach Danny?' Harpur said.

So we were all worried, and that's why Tommy's team talk, telling us how great, fabulous and wonderful Silvertown were going to be, wasn't a brilliant idea. It was the Open Cup Semi, and we were nervous enough already.

So were they.

The game slipped into a no-risks pattern right

from the start. Both teams were close-marking at the back, and playing safety balls, trying to keep possession.

'You've been watching too much TV!' Tommy yelled at us from the line.

The trouble with the keep-possession stuff the Big Teams play on TV is that they have the skill to do it, but with teams full of young players like ours it breaks down.

That's exactly what happened.

Nothing for ten minutes, and then Cyril played a square ball to Danny Mole. With Robbo in the left-back position it would have been all right, but Danny was caught napping, and their right-winger, Oates, took it off Danny's foot and got away. Oates took the ball to the edge of the area and flighted it across.

Hale, the Silvertown Number 9, was pounding in to meet it with his head. Dennis Lake spotted that Ronnie wasn't going to cut him out, so Dennis came off his line, then decided he wasn't going to make it, and hesitated.

The Number 9 got his header in, looping over Dennis's head. Cyril got to it on the line, but all he could do was to biff it into the roof of our net.

1–0 to Silvertown, and from the looks on their faces you could see they thought it was all over! They were busy wondering what their Cup Final Medals would be like.

Here's what happened:

There were three mistakes. Cyril playing the dangerous short ball without checking whether Oates had closed Danny down, Danny not cutting it out, and Dennis half coming and leaving himself stranded in no man's land.

The good thing about it was Cyril's attempted recovery, getting back to the goal-line to try his clearance. He did well to get to the ball at all . . . but we were still a goal down.

I had hardly touched the ball. My marker, Webb, was following me all over the field, which is what you get for being Top Scorer.

I've played against that before, and I know what to do. In that sort of position you are going to get clattered early on, particularly if you get the ball back-to-goal, so the trick is to play triangles with your support players, laying it off and going round the man, like this:

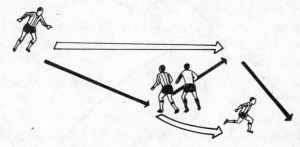

Webb knew it too.

He was an intelligent player. If he tried to crash through me from behind, he knew he could be on a booking, and so he stayed close enough to prevent me turning, but held out of the tackle and turned with me, to try and cut off the return ball.

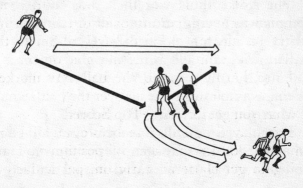

The triangle still worked, because instead of slipping the ball to me my two support players in the triangle laid it off to each other, but the effect was to cut me out.

Singhy hadn't the brains to come off his line when I pushed out, and we were getting into a mess.

'Take him right, Napper,' Tommy yelled from the touch-line.

So I did, and it worked better.

That was because on the right I had Marty Legget outside me, not Lester, and he likes coming at his man, not just using his speed to get clear.

We still didn't get much.

Lester had two runs that came to nothing, and Jezzer and I had a four-touch play in the middle that put Jezzer through, but the keeper came out and blocked him. That was about it, up front.

Our real trouble was the other end, where Dennis was having an attack of the dithers. He didn't get much to do, because Cyril Small was playing like an alligator, snapping up everything that came through. What Dennis did get, he made a muck of.

Mostly it was crosses. He palmed one on to the bar that he should have put over, although he managed to get it when it came down. Then he came out of his area and missed on a long through ball, but Oates screwed his shot from a bad angle and it ended up in the side-netting. Next Dennis came for a cross and flapped at it instead of punching. We got a free for a foul on the goalie, but really we were lucky. It could have been goal number two.

Tommy and Mr Hope were looking glum. They'd told us about the high ball to the far post, but no one thought that balls hit to the middle of the goalie's box would be a problem. Dennis usually eats them for breakfast. If Chris Taggert had been there we would have been all right, but Cyril isn't the greatest in the air. It is his back-tackling and his positional play that he gets picked for. Ronnie Purdy started going for the high balls in the centre, and that led to muddles between him and the keeper. Twice Ronnie took it off Dennis. The third time Dennis yelled his head off and Ronnie left it, and Oates nipped in and beat Dennis to the cross.

The ball slammed against the bar, and went over for a goal-kick.

Ronnie stood there with his hands on his head, glaring at Dennis.

Dennis didn't say a word. He knew he was having a bad game.

Still 1–0 down. That's the way it stayed till half-time.

'Good neat football up front, but we're getting nowhere!' Tommy said when we went in.

'Panic stations at the back!'

That about summed it up.

'Sorry,' Dennis said.

'You got us this far, son,' Tommy said. 'Remember the last one?'

That was true enough. We would never have beaten Kings Aston if Dennis hadn't turned on his World Keeper of the Year act.

'Dennis will do it for you this half!' Tommy said. 'How about some of you doing something for Dennis?'

Then he made his team changes.

Alexiou went on for Lester Singh, who'd hardly touched the ball. He wasn't getting much supply, and it didn't seem to occur to him to go looking for it himself.

Joe Fish tucked in at the back beside Cyril, with Ronnie moving into the middle beside Harpur.

'What's all that about?' Jezzer muttered to me, as we went out for the second half. 'Now we have *four* players out of position.'

I thought he was right. About the only position Alex hadn't played in our games so far was wide on the left. Danny Mole is really a centre-forward, not a left-back. Joe had been moved back when he likes coming forward, and Ronnie had been pulled out of the stopper role he likes to replace Joe. It seemed to be exactly the *wrong* way to go about winning a Cup Semifinal.

When play started, it began to make sense.

Joe is about the same in the air as Ronnie, but he has one strong advantage: he doesn't yell at the keeper. When a keeper is on form, that doesn't matter, but when he has missed a few, the last thing he needs is somebody telling him all about it.

Dennis and Joe took out the long ball to the centre of the goalie's box, and that left Silvertown trying the far post, where Tom and Danny mopped everything up, more or less. Everything in the air, that is. Silvertown were too good a team not to vary it. They tried to, but Ronnie and Harpur were getting a grip in midfield, and Silvertown couldn't get much going on the ground. Slowly, we were taking over the game.

Ronnie slotting in the middle meant we began to win more ball there, and Tommy had told Jezzer and Alex to make themselves available for Harpur, so they did. It was Ronnie-win-the-ball, side-pass to Harpur, then Harpur feeding us, or making his own runs forward.

Suddenly we were ticking. With Alex's ability to come inside instead of hugging the line like Lester, I was able to draw Webb right across the width of the field, bringing both wings into it.

'You can lose him this half, Napper!' Tommy had said to me, and that's the way it turned out.

Twice I got clear of Webb. The first time I went through on my own, drew the keeper, and squared the ball across for Jezzer to walk it in, our usual routine. Jezzer decided to go for glory and blasted it straight over the bar. The next time I got clear down the middle, drew their last man on to me, and put Marty Legget through. The keeper came off his line and blocked Marty's shot, and their defender got in to turn the rebound behind for a corner kick.

The Silvertown manager was up off the bench, yelling, and then he pulled one of their front men off, and sent a big kid called Jull on in the Number 14 shirt.

He ran over to Webb, and from then on the two of them were following me about!

Twenty-five minutes to go, and they were still one up, but we had bottled their attack, and they'd settled for a result ... that is what the extra defender seemed to mean. Maybe they hadn't much choice, because we had them under so much pressure. The danger was that we would do a Kings Aston, and began to panic because we couldn't score. They were like us, they had defenders who could soak up pressure. We knew the way to beat them was to keep playing the game our way, building up from the back, and not go mad.

Tommy switched Ronnie back, and brought

Joe forward into his original position . . . that meant *six* of us coming at them, and great big gaps were appearing in the middle. Tommy had told me to go wide, and my two followed me, with Alex and Marty coming inside to link up with Jezz.

Harpur got on the ball, coming out of our half. I was left, Marty was wide right, Jezzer running across the defence, Joe Fish steaming through from behind. Harpur kept on . . . and on . . . and on . . . then, at the last moment, with the defenders waking up too late, he played a ball straight through them and there was Joe cutting through the stationary defenders. Joe timed his run perfectly, to coincide with the moment when the defence had to stop backing off Harpur, catching them square.

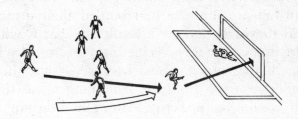

GOAL! GOAL! GOAL!

1–1. We were back in the game, with fifteen minutes left.

They'd taken a gamble on holding what they'd got, and it hadn't worked. Once a team has committed to that kind of pattern, it isn't easy to break it.

Their second sub, Swinson, came on in the Number 12. He was big, and we thought we'd be in trouble on the long ball again. He got clear twice, but each time Tom Brocken managed to catch him and cut out the danger. Swinson had no pace. We reckoned that was why he was on the bench and not in the starting line-up.

The third time he got the ball, about twenty metres out, he didn't try to take Tom on. He poked the ball a metre in front of him and WHAM!

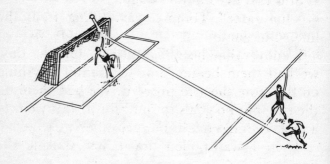

It was a real pile-driver, but Dennis tipped it over when it looked an all-the-way winner.

That was it as far as the sub was concerned. He knew he was beaten for the pace by all our back men, and his thing was his wham-shot. The problem was that he had very little idea where it was going when he hit it, and we spotted that he was one-footed. That made him easier to close down, and he began to drift out of it.

Marty Legget got through, and the keeper came out and saved.

Harpur had a shot that glanced off the bar and went for a goal-kick.

Marty was pulled down outside the box and Tom Brocken took one of his blasters at the free, but the ball went wide.

I got clear of both my markers and squared it across to Joe Fish, and he headed into the keeper's arms when it must have been easier to score.

Still 1–1, five minutes to go.

'Our game!' Tommy was yelling from the line. 'Our game!'

I know what he was thinking. On the day, we had them beaten, but we hadn't anything on the score sheet to prove it. We had them on the run, but no goals to show for it. If it went to a replay, things might be very different.

Then I was pulled down, just outside the box.

Free kick.

Tom Brocken headed up to take it, but Harpur grabbed the ball.

'Mine, Tom,' he said, and placed the ball.

Then he looked at me, and nodded three times.

Secret Sign Number Five. It went right back

to our days at Red Row, when we played together and had all kinds of routines for free kicks. Tommy Cowans wasn't keen on them at our level, he said time enough for that later, we'd only get muddled up.

I trotted back to Cyril, followed by my markers, happily coming out of defence. I nodded three times, and suddenly Cyril was grinning all over his face.

Number Five used to be called the Small Special when we were at Red Row, but we hadn't used it for years!

Harpur took the kick.

I'd doubled back, taking both markers with me, and at the last moment I headed for the near post, where Jezzer and Tom Brocken were already positioned, yelling like mad.

Harpur slung the ball to the far post, and there was Cyril coming in from the edge of the area where he'd been lurking.

Here is how it worked:

It looked like a bad ball, over-hit for Marty, who was queuing up on that side. The reason was that it wasn't meant for him.

Cyril, arriving late and wide, headed down for the bottom corner.

GOAL! GOAL! GOAL!

2-1 to us!

Cyril slid into the net after the ball, grabbed it, and booted it up in the air in delight, and the next moment we were all on top of him.

Silvertown couldn't believe it. They'd been busy watching the high-ball specialists in our team, with the notion that Cyril was only on the edge of the area to pick up any half-clearance. His late, wide run caught them off guard, and before they knew where they were, the ball was in the net, and they were out of the Open Cup.

They were, too. The goal seemed to finish them.

Right at the end, Marty Legget got on to another through ball from Joe Fish, and slotted it home.

3-1 to us, and the Final Whistle!

An old Red Row trick that we hadn't used for years had got us in the Open Cup Final. We had beaten the two top teams in the Premier League on the way and nobody had been able to stop us.

Old Cyril was in the centre circle doing his Cyril-dance and everybody was going mad.

ASTON CRASH IN LEAGUE CUP DECIDER!
TREBLE FOR THE VILLA?

Premier kingpins Kings Aston crashed to a shock 3–0 defeat in the replay of the Brontley League Cup (Jack Dade Trophy) at Hume on Saturday . . . and it was no fluke.

Elm Villa, the season's surprise packet from the League's First Division, outplayed a full-strength Aston team in every department of the game. Striker Mark Lamprey notched two goals on either side of half-time, and Hatch's eighty-sixth-minute penalty goal after a foul on Lamprey only added the icing to the cake!

Elm Villa are poised for the Treble now, with the First Division title already in the bag, and an upcoming Open Cup Final clash with Warne County Colts.

Can Elm Villa do it? Tommy Cowans' Warne side will be no easy meat, with their confidence high after narrowly defeating Silvertown and Kings Aston in earlier rounds. I feel that the overall power-play of the impressive Villa side makes them favourites to take the Trophy, and thus complete their treble . . . but only just.

Look at Colts' record . . . billed as the 'lucky' team of the competition, and consistently underrated by their opponents, Colts have taken on all comers and won, despite their lack of regular competitive match practice. They seem to improve with each performance, and their present form suggests that they would have been a major force in the Premier Division this season, possibly *the* major force, had they not fallen foul of the rules and been forced out of the competition on a technicality.

Looks like a great Final!

10. Game Plan

Tommy got us all together in the dressing-room after training, to sort things out for the Final.

They needed sorting out! For a start, Marty Legget was ruled out, so that was our right side attack gone. Matty was out as well, and Robbo still had the bad knee. We only had seventeen players to pick from, because of the K. Dooley business, and with Ally Scott's long-term injury, that brought us down to sixteen. Sixteen, minus the three short-term casualties meant that we could only just manage a team and two subs. Danny Mole came in for Marty Legget on the right side, which made sense, and Lester was picked for another go, wide on the left, despite being taken off and replaced by Alex in the Semi.

Alex was one sub, and Dennis Lake was the other. A keeper as sub! A not-too-pleased sub, either, because Dennis had played in all our Open Cup-ties up to the Final, and now Tony Bantam had come in to take his place.

'You've done nothing wrong, Dennis,'

Tommy told him. 'But Elm Villa live on the high ball played short into the box, where you have been having trouble. Tony's best point is the way he comes off his line, so he has to be in. Sorry, kiddo!'

He wasn't as sorry as Dennis was! Nobody liked it, not even Tony Bantam. But what could Tony say? Tommy had to pick the team, and it was probably the right choice. Dennis would never have been in the side at all if Tony hadn't been injured. Tony had proved his fitness in our friendlies after the Semi, and there was no doubt in anybody's mind who the better keeper was.

'It still doesn't seem fair,' Cyril said. 'Tony in goal, and old Lester back on the wing, when Dennis and Alex have been playing well. They both ought to be in.'

They couldn't be in without somebody else being left out. Lester was the real gamble, because we would be relying on his speed to counter-attack. We had done that in the Semi-final, and had to take him off, because he hadn't got a sniff of the ball. If he couldn't do it in the Semi, why did Tommy think he would in the Final?

'Because Elm Villa have to push forward,' Harpur said. 'Their whole game is based on it. So there will be room at the back, and if Lester gets room to move nobody will catch him. They

144

aren't like Kings Aston or Silvertown, who can vary things a bit. It is Route One all the time. They can't do anything else, and so far they have done it so well that they've walked away with everything!'

'We're leaving out a good footballer who works for the team, and putting in a racehorse,' Cyril said.

'Well, we can pull Lester off if it doesn't work out,' Harpur said, not very hopefully. The trouble was that we might not be able to afford a tactical substitution, because then we would only have a goalie on the bench to act as cover for any outfield injury.

'Route One team!' Tommy kept on telling us. 'Two big men down the middle, two big men at the back, and the goalie didn't get his nickname for nothing. The ball is going to be falling in our goal-mouth from a great height, which is all right, because we have it sorted!'

If we had, we'd be the first team in the Brontley League to manage it.

'They play it very simple,' Tommy said. 'Big up-and-unders from the back, on to Hatch and Lamprey. Isolen and Parson coming wide and fast to pick them up, Danny Cole as the knock-back man, Lowe as the provider. Big strong hoofers the lot of them! It shouldn't work against a better team, but so far no one they've played has been able to cope with it. Why?

Because they play it very, very well. Route One suits their players, that is why they play it. They are good at it! What that means is that we mustn't let them play it. So what do we do?'

He'd been telling us all week. *'Cut off the supply.'* That was the theory. Close down the back four and stop them launching their aerial bombardment. *'Block the two front men.'* That meant Chris Taggert and Ronnie Purdy close-marking them and going for everything with them. *'First to the ball when they lay it off.'* That meant Cyril lying just behind our two central defenders to cut out the flicks-through, and Joe Fish and Harpur making sure that they cut out Isolen and Parson coming wide, with Jezz and Danny Mole taking centre midfield. *'Hit them on the break.'* That meant Lester and I were to stay upfield, out of it. The way Elm Villa played, everyone piled forward, and the theory was that Lester's speed would be our big weapon. It was my job to get on the end of anything he could put over.

That was the theory.

The problem was that all the other teams they'd come up against must have worked out something similar, and it hadn't worked for them, so why should it work for us?

'Because we're a better team than any of the others!' Cyril said.

'Look at Elm Villa's results!' Tom Brocken

said glumly. '3–0 against Kings Aston in the League Cup replay. *And* the Kings were at full strength.'

'Y-e-s,' I said. 'But Kings Aston had gone off the boil. They had been winning all season, and then we beat them, and Allentown beat them. They were punch-drunk by the time they met Elm Villa.'

I hoped that was it, anyway.

'All this talk before the game, and it looks as if we are going to play to suit them!' Cyril grumbled. 'What we want to do is to keep the ball on the ground, and make them play *our* way.'

'That's what we will do,' Harpur said.

'Only we have lost our right-winger and Tom won't be able to get up. Harpur and Joe Fish will be two on four in the midfield unless Danny Mole and Jezzer drop back, and if they drop back we won't have a forward line!' Cyril said. 'It's silly. We will end up playing four across the middle of the park, with only two up front. That is the way *they* play it, and they are used to it. We play it neat in midfield, not just punching balls forward for two strikers to run on to. They'll eat us.'

'Wrong!' Harpur said. 'They play it hitting long balls and missing out the midfield. Joe and I will be *carrying* the ball forward, linking up with Danny and Napper and Jezz. We'll buzz all over them, and force them back.'

'So where does old Lester come in?' Cyril objected. 'He's only there to go on long chases. If we play all this short midfield stuff, he'll be ornamental.'

'If he comes off, he gives us a long-ball option,' Harpur said. 'We can play it long, or short. They won't know which way we'll choose. Long to Lester, with Napper getting on the end of his crosses, or short passing through the middle. We have the skill to vary our game, they haven't! That's why we're going to win.'

'Well, I hope so!' Cyril said.

He wasn't the only one!

Brontley League
OPEN CUP FINAL

Elm Villa

Warne County Colts

SWINLEY PARK
KO 3 p.m.

PRODUCTION OF THIS PROGRAMME SPONSORED BY
THE BRONTLEY BUILDING SOCIETY

Up for the Cup!

On behalf of the Executive of the Brontley League I would like to welcome both teams, their Managers and supporters to Swinley Park Stadium today for the Final of the Brontley League Open Cup.

For the boys selected to play, this will be the biggest test of their lives. Some may go on to greater things, but today, for them, is *the* match.

I am sure that everyone wishes them well, and that we all look forward to a great game of football.

Once again, a **Big Thank You** to the Brontley Building Society, who have made this match, this programme, and all the events sponsored by the League possible.

Now on with the game!

H. Metcalfe (League Secretary)

Pen-pictures of Today's Teams

WARNE COUNTY COLTS

Lake, D. (Goalkeeper) Lightly built Dennis came in halfway through the season, and has impressed with his overall ability.

Bantam, T. (Goalkeeper) Last year's inter-league choice, injury has sidelined Tony for most of the season, but he may challenge for a place today.

Brocken, T. Slow on the turn, but impressive going forward, Skipper Tom has been a tower of strength in Colts' defence.

Purdy, R. A strong tackler and ball-winner who never knows when he is beaten. Sure to be in the thick of things!

Small, C. One of three 'Red Row Stars', Cyril is ideal cover for the back-line defenders. Scored the decisive goal in the Semi versus Silvertown.

Mole, D. Play-anywhere Danny has slotted into the defence in the absence of the injured Robinson.

Fish, J. Makes up for slight lack of pace and height by his astute positional play.

Brown, H. Harpur, another 'Red Row Star', is the playmaker of the Colts side, but can also play his part defensively.

Taggert, C. A new signing for Colts this season. May be sidelined for today's match by illness.

Legget, M. Fast and tricky wide player, with an eye for goal.

Jezz, A. 'Jezzer' was on the fringe of inter-league selection last season. A hot shot, he combines well with McCann.

McCann, B. 'Napper', the third 'Red Row Star', is Top Scorer for the Colts, and can expect to be close-marked today.

Singh, L. A speedy left-sided player, sometimes drifts out of the game, but always a danger to defences.

Matthews, C. An old-style central striker who uses his height and weight to great advantage.

Alexiou, D. Play-anywhere performer, with ability on the ball.

ELM VILLA

Belmont, M. (Goalkeeper) 'Bomber', first-choice keeper up to the last few weeks, when injury cost him his place. Brilliant on his day.

Williams, B. (Goalkeeper) 'Baz', sound and capable keeper with the ability to turn in a good performance when it matters.

Chenhall, H. Strong and resolute tackler, likes to break forward in aid of his attack.

Lowe, R. 'Rabby', a thoughtful playmaker, often the player around whom things revolve for Villa.

Robson, T. Anchorman in the give-away-nothing role, likely to take on Colts' two central strikers.

Wayne, G. George plays just in front of Robson, and the two form a perfect combination. Both strong, both tall.

Winecker, D. Slight for a midfielder, but on his day a matchwinner. May start on the bench.

Cole, D. 'Dazz', sturdy and adaptable, often underrated, but ever-present in the side.

Cole, M. Miles, brother of 'Dazz', likes to probe forward, and will test Colts' back line, given half a chance.

Parson, E. Eric is an out-and-out winger, fast and elusive, with a good shot in both feet.

Hatch, H. Harry plays as foil to Mark Lamprey. Has good all-round ability, and a formidable strike rate.

Lamprey, M. With nineteen goals this season, Mark is the obvious Villa danger man. Tall and fast.

Isolen, Z. Yet another striker who can play wide man in an emergency, or straight down the park.

Higginbotham, S. 'Stevie' is the ideal sub. He can slot in at the back, midfield, or lead the line. Has a keen eye for goal.

Corner, L. Les normally plays in the back four and is a solid if unspectacular defender, a little short of pace.

HOW THEY REACHED THE FINAL:

WARNE COUNTY COLTS
Allentown	4–2	McCann 3, Brocken
Barnsdale	9–0	Jezz 3, Brocken 2, McCann 2, Singh, Lake (pen.)
Kings Aston	1–0	Purdy
Silvertown	3–1	Fish, Small, Legget

ELM VILLA
Blyth County	4–0	Lamprey 2, Hatch 2
Coatbridge	3–0	Lamprey 2, Parson
Romsey	6–0	Hatch 2, Winecker, Robson, Parson, Lamprey
BYC	4–1	Lamprey, Hatch, Corner. Opponents, o.g.,1

11. Final Whistle

The big, b-i-g, b-i-g-g-e-s-t game ever in the history of N. McCann Demon Goalscorer Super Star, taking on George Wayne, Elm Villa's Stopper King, in a personal battle that might decide who won the Cup!

'It's not just about you, it's about the team!' Harpur said, when I was rabbiting on. 'You and Cyril, you both think the same way!

It was easy for him to say, but the way we were playing it I was likely to be front runner all on my own a lot of the time, and I thought if I could put one over on their stopper it would change the whole game.

'Get a hat trick, Napper!' my silly sister Avril said, when we were standing outside the ground. Everyone was there, all the old Red Row Stars, because they had read about Harpur and Cyril and me in the *Dispatch*, and they all wanted to be there on our Big Day.

'You couldn't buy a hat to fit his Big Head!' Avril's friend Ugly Irma Bankworth said, but I didn't even chase her.

I was too worried about the match and not-having-slept-properly, because I hadn't, and whether George Wayne would be all over me in the first ten minutes and I would be right out of it and they would bomb our goal all day and win about 5–0. I think we were all the same. Nobody in the team got a good night's sleep.

Then it was all hurry, changing and out on to the field, and before we knew it we were lined up to kick off in the Brontley League Open Cup Final against the odds-on favourites, Elm Villa.

This is how the two teams lined up on the Big Day:

WARNE COUNTY COLTS

Bantam
Brocken Purdy Taggert Small
Fish Brown
Mole Jezz McCann Singh
Subs: Lake, Alexiou

Hatch Lamprey
Parson Cole (D.) Lowe Isolen
Cole (M.) Robson Wayne Chenhall
Belmont

Subs: Winecker, Corner

ELM VILLA

The ref tossed up, and Tom Brocken won, so they had kick-off.

Straight back to Lowe, and he played the long ball we'd been told about, right to the edge of our box, where Chris Taggert met it, climbing above Hatch.

Chris got real power in his header, and it fell to Joe Fish, who carried it forward to the half-way line, where Cole went at him.

Tom Brocken was steaming up from right back, so Joe feinted to turn the ball inside to Jezzer and then slipped it wide, and suddenly Tom was breaking clear into their half.

He was supposed to carry it, because we had planned to work the ball on the ground, the idea being that Jezzer and I had very little hope of getting the ball in the air from their two central defenders, Robson and Wayne. I was running just wide of Wayne, outside their box on the left, and Jezzer was belting right, expecting a through ball when Tom had Parson committed to the tackle, but Tom just thumped it.

Their tactic, not ours, a snow-gatherer of a ball deep into their box, easy picking for their big keeper. Wayne eased up, and yelled for him to come.

The ball was coming out of the sun. Maybe the keeper lost it, I don't know. Whatever it was, the keeper stayed rooted on his line. Wayne

155

had stopped moving and I nipped inside him, with Robson charging across too late to cut off the danger.

I thought about heading it, then thought better. I met the ball chest-high, a metre inside the box, took it, knocked it past Robson and I was on for goal, with the keeper waking up and coming. I didn't have time to think about chipping him or side-stepping him. I just hit it! He dived and got a hand to the ball, but it spun up and over the line just as Wayne crashed into me, with a thigh-high late tackle that was more of a bull charge than a tackle, laying me flat on the ground.

GOAL! GOAL! GOAL! G-o-a-l!

A Napper McCann Demon Goalscorer Ace Super Strike in the very first minute of the match with my very first touch ... well, not quite . . . I'd controlled it and knocked it past Robson and then hit it . . . but who cares!

GOAL! GOAL! GOAL! GOAL!

I tried to get up, but everybody was mobbing me and our spectators were going wild and somebody jumped on my back and I went down, and this time I stayed down.

My left leg was gone.

I could hardly feel it. The ref got them off me and Mr Hope and Tommy were on and there was whole crowd of players arguing. Ronnie Purdy was having a go at Wayne, so Tom Brocken grabbed Ronnie and held his arms down.

It was a muddle. When Wayne went into me his shoulder caught my jaw and my teeth rattled and I was all fuddled up, but not so fuddled up that I didn't known I'd SCORED! It was about all I did know.

It was really, really, really rotten.

They made me stand up, and I could move the leg, and bend it, though it was stiff, and suddenly after not hurting at all it was very, very sore.

'What about the head?' the ref said. 'Concussion?'

'I'm OK,' I said. 'Really and truly.'

Concussion is the one thing they always take you off for, and I hadn't got concussion, but I didn't know if they would believe me.

Tommy was on, and Alex was running up and down the line, ready to take my place.

'Give you ten minutes, son, see if you can run it off,' Tommy said.

I thought, *Great! I'm on and I haven't been subbed and it's OK!*

But it wasn't.

Tommy put me wide on the right, so I would be in front of the dug-out and he could keep an eye on me. Danny slotted into the centre.

I tried to move for the first ball that came, but I couldn't make it. The ball ran in to touch, and I was nowhere near it.

'Other side! Other side!' Tommy was yelling to the others from the touch-line. He had Alex beside him, doing toe-touches, and stripped off ready to come on.

I had to keep moving. If they saw I couldn't move, I would be off. The ref kept over to my side, checking that I was all right. Concussion is the one thing they are really hot on, because it can be so serious. I knew I hadn't got concussion, but they didn't.

I think I would have been off if we hadn't had the only-one-real-sub problem. Tommy knew that if he put Alex on and we copped another injury, he would be stuck with only Dennis Lake to put on, and we would be virtually down to ten men for the rest of the match.

'Funnel back, Napper,' Tom shouted at me.

'Hold the wing for me if you can.'

He moved inside, still covering the wing, but slotting in behind Ronnie. I was left trying to pick up Parson. That was tricky, because I knew I couldn't keep pace with my leg, so I came off him, lying deep, but blocking his run for goal. I hoped that my just being there would make him push the ball past me, and give Tom extra time to pick him up. I thought it was probably the best I could do till the pain went out of the leg.

Miles Cole was alive to it.

He could see that the balance of our team was all wrong on the right, so he started slinging the ball wide. In a funny way it was good, because it took the pressure off our two centre-backs, and it *made* me move. Moving didn't make the leg not hurt, but I began to get more confident that I could do something after all, and wouldn't have to be substituted.

First Parson got the ball deep in our half and went inside me, and I nicked it off him. The next time he didn't come close but he pushed it past and ran round me, which I couldn't do much about. I brought him down and they got a free kick.

'Watch it, son,' the ref said.

'OK,' I said.

'How's the head?' he said anxiously.

I was lucky really. If he hadn't been

concerned about concussion I might have got a booking for the tackle, but I didn't. *Lucky*. My luck was a bit mixed. I'd scored a goal, but I wasn't much use to the team now. I didn't feel very lucky.

Miles Cole took the free kick.

It was a cleverly flighted ball to the back post, just the edge of the goalie's box, with Hatch and Lamprey and Wayne all thundering in to meet it.

Tony Bantam was off his line like a flash. He met the ball with a clean punch, just as they crashed into him. The ref's whistle went, Tony was on the ground and Tommy had his head in his hands. Mr Hope sprinted across the field and Dennis Lake was up out of the dug-out grabbing his gloves.

It was all right.

Lamprey got the yellow card for taking Tony in mid-air, and Tony got his breath back and was able to take the free kick, with Tommy yelling at Ronnie Purdy and Chris Taggert to give the keeper cover the next time.

It was a great save really, though the free kick made it not look like one. If Tony hadn't come they would have had three men in for a clear header at goal.

'He's got guts, our keeper!' Tom Brocken said to me. 'Trouble is, he's going to need them.'

160

Now that I was coming more into it and keeping a check on Parson, Miles Cole began to switch it. Chris Taggert was holding his own against Lamprey, but Hatch was making mincemeat out of Ronnie Purdy, who was beginning to lose his cool.

Cole had spotted it, and he started yelling at big Lowe, who was their chief provider, to thump the ball in at Hatch. The only thing we could do about that was to try to cut off the supply. Jezzer couldn't cope with Lowe, so Danny Mole switched back from striker to try to sort him out. It was muscle against muscle, and Lowe won, mostly, but not by much. Anyway, the move limited the damage at the back.

It didn't help much at the front.

I was out of it still, not able to get up sufficient pace to get forward, and Tom was too worried about Parson beating me to risk any runs, so we had nothing on the right at all. Lester was seeing the ball all right, and he got in two or three runs at big Chenhall, but he didn't get a lot of change out of them. Their big back four were dominating everything, with Jezzer reduced to chasing and trying to cut down their options. Their goalie was bombing us with huge balls right up the middle every time he got his hands on it . . . not that he did everything from the hands. He was a roll-the-ball-out-of-the-

161

area-and-then-belt-it merchant, and with everybody pressed back he had plenty of space to
do it.

It was all backs-to-the-wall stuff, with Elm
Villa showing everybody why they were unbeaten. They'd gone a goal down in the first
minute, but they hadn't folded when I put us in
front. They kept pumping the ball upfield and
chasing at us.

Not *scoring* though.

Tony Bantam was on the end of everything,
dominating his area, and what he didn't get
Chris Taggert was coping with, or Ronnie was
scrambling away.

Hatch on Ronnie was the big problem. Any
time Lamprey beat Chris in the air, it was an
automatic flick on to Hatch. That made it
Ronnie's job to stop him, or Cyril's to pick
Hatch off if Ronnie couldn't cope, and it was
nearly all down to Cyril. The bonus for us was
that Cyril was having one of his good Cyril
days, and when Cyril is good he is very good.
Three times he got to Hatch, once he blocked a
shot that had goal all over it, and twice he
managed to get in a saving tackle. That was
fine, but Ronnie knew Cyril was doing his job,
and that only made Ronnie worse. Twice he
scythed Hatch down close to the box, giving
away free kicks, and earning himself a yellow
card and a talking-to in the process.

Tony Bantam came and took the first free kick cleanly off Lamprey's head. On the second one Tony came, mistimed his punch, and Ronnie got in to turn the ball for a corner. It would have been a goal if their Number 7, Isolen, had been sharper. Ronnie did really well to get to it first, but it was his tackle that had caused it in the first place.

Tom Brocken yelled at Ronnie and Cyril to switch, so that Cyril went on Hatch, but that didn't work.

The corner came across, and Hatch was all over Cyril in the air, heading the ball down against the foot of our post, where it went the right way for a goal-kick, instead of back across the goal, where they could hardly have helped scoring.

Two more snow-scrapers from Belmont, who was wandering further and further out of his goal, and each time Hatch went up over Cyril and headed them on. The first time Tony came sprawling off his line to save at Lamprey's feet, and the second Tom Brocken managed to come inside and clear for another corner.

The corner came over.

Hatch and Cyril again.

Hatch rose way over Cyril, and got a header in on goal, but Tony took it as if he could take those all day, and almost in the same movement he booted the ball upfield.

Wayne had been up for the corner, so it was Chenhall who went to meet it with Lester Singh. We thought it was odds-on Chenhall, because he'd been more or less on top of the winger, but Singhy did really well, and dummied him.

Here's how he did it:

Chenhall was beaten, the power of his own run leaving him completely wrong-footed, and Singhy was clear, and motoring down the wing, with Danny Mole heading for the centre.

Lester booted the ball on, too far, and then it was a race with Belmont pounding out of his goal and Danny yelling for the cross and Lester sprinting for it. Lester made it, steered it past the keeper, found his shot blocked by Chenhall, who'd recovered enough to get back goal-side, and spotted Danny all alone on the edge of the area, in the centre.

All he had to do was play it gently across.

Lester hit it.

He made a complete mess of it. The ball was hit so hard that it went right across the area, way over Danny's head, into no man's land out on the right.

Lester's ball was so bad that it wrong-footed all the defenders who'd been steaming back.

N. McCann, half-speed Super Star, was the only one who hadn't a hope of making it into the area to get on the end of a decent cross . . . but it wasn't a decent cross, it was a complete mess of a cross, landing nowhere near where he'd meant to hit it.

Right in front of me!

Absolutely clear, on my lonesome, about thirty metres from goal, wide on the right, and hopelessly out of position because I couldn't run properly.

An empty goal, with the keeper belting back and the defenders on the turn.

Here's the position:

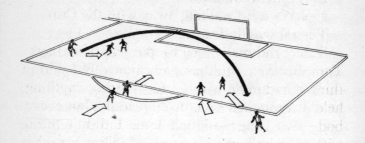

There were too many bodies in the way for me to have any hope of threading it through them from that range, so I did the only thing I could do, throwing in a long lob at the goal, miles high over everyone.

This is what happened next:

G-o-a-l!

Another Napper Super Strike! Two goals in the Cup Final! It was the goalie who knocked it in the end, but that doesn't make any difference because I spotted it and I hit it and I scored a Super Goal when I couldn't even move fast enough to keep up with the play.

Everyone went mad!

2–0! We were walking away with the Cup!

Then it was half-time.

'Lester did really well to spot you lying back,' Tom Brocken said, as we came off. I didn't think it had to do with Lester spotting anything, he'd just miscued his cross hopelessly, but everybody was congratulating him. I didn't mind, with everybody running around telling me what a brilliant finish it was. For that matter I hadn't been lying back, I just couldn't run fast enough to get upfield to where I should have been . . . and if I had been where I should have been, I wouldn't have scored! Lucky again.

I spent half-time having my leg massaged, so I didn't hear what Tommy was telling them. He came into the physio's room and said what great goals I'd got and asked if I was fit to go on, because two or three of the others were carrying knocks and he didn't want to risk being left with only Dennis Lake as sub, once he had used Alex.

'I'm all right,' I said.

'Fit enough to try down the middle again?' he said.

'Yes,' I said.

And that was it.

'It's all wrapped up!' Cyril said, chewing away at his gum. 'All we have to do is hold them!'

All.

They went straight down the field from the kick-off, laying the ball back to the keeper, who rolled it out of his area and then hit us with a long one.

Hatch got up over Cyril and headed it sideways to Lamprey, but Ronnie Purdy stuck out his hand and pushed the ball away. I don't think he meant to do it, it was just instinctive, but we thought he would be sent off, because he'd already had a yellow card in the first half. In an ordinary match I think he would have been, but maybe the ref gave him the benefit of the doubt because it was Cup Final, and it wasn't a clear-cut case of preventing a goal.

Penalty.

Tony had no chance with Lamprey's kick.

1–2.

'Get in it! Get in it!' Tommy was yelling.

The funny thing was that their goal got us going. 2–0 seemed enough of a cushion, but 2–1 meant we had to do something, and for the first time in the match Joe Fish and Harpur began to slow things down, playing the ball around. Elm Villa were still on top, but Jezzer and I were getting going, inter-passing and bringing Danny and Lester into the game.

We got close two or three times, and that seemed to give everybody confidence. Tom Brocken managed to overlap Danny from the back and got a cross over, and I had a header for my hat trick, but Wayne went up my back and I headed wide. Then Lester had a run, and fired into the side-netting, when I had managed to get clear of Wayne.

Wayne was getting the needle.

It was tricky for him. He'd messed up in the first minute and managed to get the yellow card for his late challenge on me, which he deserved because it put me out of the game for most of the first half, but now I'd moved back on to him he was in trouble.

'Take him on, Napper!' Mr Hope had told me coming up the tunnel, and he was right. Every time I got near the box with the ball I had a go at him, because he had to be in two minds about lifting me again. If he tackled all out and missed, we'd be on a penalty and he would get the red card, but if he didn't tackle all out he knew I had the skill to go round him.

Jezzer spotted what was happening, and dropped back a few metres, taking Robson with him, so that I was on the end of most things. We weren't playing to have Wayne sent off, just using his own bad tackles against him.

We had exactly the same problem at the other end with Ronnie, who doesn't know how to half-tackle anybody. Every time their long balls landed, Ronnie was caught in two minds, so in the end Tommy had to do something. He switched Danny Mole back into defence, and put Ronnie wide on the right.

It seemed a good move, because Ronnie had been struggling, and Danny is good in the air, which is where we were taking the pummelling.

That's what we thought.

Then Miles Cole fooled everybody by running on instead of thumping in his usual sky-ball, and Danny, committing himself late when he realized the danger, bowled him clean over in the box. It was a forward-playing-as-a-defender tackle, the kind of thing that was always likely to happen to Danny, so Tommy's good move had backfired with a vengeance.

Another penalty, and another booking!

Tony saved the first shot, but it had to be retaken when Cyril encroached, and the second time Hatch sent Tony the wrong way, and tucked the ball neatly away in the left-hand corner.

2—2.

We'd scored two goals when they were on top, first half, and now they'd scored two goals when we were on top . . . well, not on top, but almost.

'Keep playing your football!' Tommy bawled from the line. We'd let a two-goal lead slip, and he must have been tearing his hair out.

'Calm it. Calm it. Calm it!' Mr Hope shouted.

Tom Brocken started talking at the back. He switched Danny wide to take Parson, who had drifted out of the game, and he moved inside himself, to help with the high balls.

It was an almost obvious move, but we had been too worried down the right in the first half to think of it. The combination of Tom, Chris and Cyril Small began to get on top of Hatch and Lamprey. It was three on two for every high ball, with Danny nipping in to cover the nick-ons, and suddenly they were going no-where, and they knew it.

Sub!

Parson went off, and Winecker came on, but he didn't go down the right.

Instead, they put him deep, and almost at once he changed the pattern of their play. He was spraying the ball about on the floor, wide to the wings, and coming through for the return with Miles Cole and Isolen backing him up. The good news was that *we* had forced them to change their tactics. The bad news was that Winecker was doing everything right. He was really good, a cross between Harpur at laying balls on and Marty Legget in his ability to get on the end of things. I don't know why he wasn't on from the start.

Suddenly, their two main strikers being

hustled off the high ball didn't seem important any more. Winecker kept feeding Isolen, and twice Isolen got through and wasted good chances. The third time they worked it Winecker steamed into the box himself and got in a header, but Tony Bantam killed it with a Super Save.

Tommy was up on the line, shouting at Ronnie, and the next thing we knew Ronnie had come off the wing, and was trailing Winecker. It was good, because Winecker liked to start from a deep position, and that meant Ronnie wasn't doing his thing round the box, and also because Winecker didn't like being tackled. Twice he wound up on the floor with Ronnie moving off upfield on the ball, and that was the last we saw of him.

They'd switched their tactics, and we'd countered them, so the game was going our way again.

They switched Isolen across with Winecker, to try to take Ronnie off him, but Ronnie had his orders, and he trotted across the left, where he ran the show. Suddenly Ronnie was winning the ball and putting Lester clear.

Down the line, and Lester shot wide over the goal from miles out, with nothing on.

Down the line, and he muffed his centre, straight to Wayne.

Down the line, and he elected to play the ball back to Ronnie, when I was clear.

172

Down the line, and he ran the ball in to touch.

Tommy had had enough. Apart from the miskick that led to our second goal, Lester had done nothing, and he was wasting all the possession that Ronnie was winning for us. Tommy turned up on the touch-line with Alex beside him, clutching the Number 11 card.

Alex on, Lester off.

Then he spotted Danny Mole, lying on his back on the edge of the area, and clutching his arm.

Quick change of plan. Danny's shoulder was dislocated or something, so it was Danny off, and Alex on. Alex went to the back, and we were left with Lester doing nothing out wide.

It was virtually ten men, but we were still on top. The long ball hadn't worked, and Winecker coming on to spray the ball about hadn't worked, and they had nothing left to throw at us because Corner, the other sub, was just a defender. They could have taken Wayne off, but I think they thought that Wayne worried about a red card was still a better bet than Corner.

Five minutes to go. 2–2, and the game was still anybody's.

Just time for me to get my third, a brilliant hat trick that won the Cup for Colts.

It didn't happen.

They went down the far end and threw in another long ball to Hatch, because they couldn't think of anything else, and he got up over Tony Bantam and headed just over the bar, when everybody thought he was going to get the winner.

Tony took the goal-kick.

Jezzer got it. He played it to me and ran on. I played it back to him, inside Chenhall who was tracking back. Jezzer took the ball in his stride and hit it, WHACK, from about twenty metres out.

Belmont made a fabulous save, leaping right across the goal and taking the ball two-handed, when most other goalies would just have watched it crash into the net.

Everybody was roaring and clapping him, and we were all running back to cover his clearance, which is what we seemed to have been doing all day.

Belmont rolled the ball out of his area, really bouncing with confidence.

He rolled it too far.

He had been doing it all day without any problem.

What he didn't spot was old Singhy, who was coming in like a train, from his blind side. Singhy nicked the ball off Belmont, trundled into the area, and rolled it into the back of the net.

GOAL!

GOAL!

174

GOAL!

3–2 with only two or three minutes to go!

An amazing old mess-up of a goal scored by the one player on our team who couldn't be bothered to go back covering anybody, but had the speed to take advantage of the goalie's silly mistake. To be fair to Lester, I don't think anyone else on our team would have had the speed to make it to the ball, and that is what he was in the team for, but it was still a daft goal to win a Cup Final with!

That's what it did.

We WON! We won the Open Cup on Lester's silly goal, 3–2 against the best team in the competition, who were odds-on favourites to win!

It shouldn't have happened that way.

I should have won it with the third goal to make my hat trick; or Harpur should have worked one with our Red Row Secret Signs; or Jezzer should have nipped on to something, the way he had been doing all season; or Tom should have won it with a rocket from far out.

No way! It was old Lester-the-Jester!

Nobody cared. We'd won – w-o-n! Cyril did his Dance in the centre circle and then we went up the steps in the stand and Tom Brocken got the Cup and waved it over his head and I got the base and waved that and we all got our medals. My mum was crying in the stand, with Miss Fellows, who used to be my teacher mopping Mum's tears for her, and she was hugging my dad and Avril. It was the biggest, best, most exciting moment in my Football Career.

'Wait till next season, Napper!' Mr Hope said, when I told him it was. 'Anything might happen!'

'E-N-G-L-A-N-D! E-N-G-L-A-N-D!' Cyril started chanting, and then he remembered he'd have to get in the Manchester team first and changed it to 'U-N-I-T-E-D! U-N-I-T-E-D!'

'Colts will do for me!' Harpur said, grinning.

That's the last thing I remember about our Big Day. Cyril shouting and dancing, and old Harpur cool as a cucumber, clutching his Cup-winner's medal, and Ally Scott and Dennis Lake, who might have been in our team but didn't make it, cheering and shouting like everybody else. Tommy, Mr Hope, all the team . . . all except K. Dooley, who was D. Dooley and almost did us in. It must have been tough for him, wanting to be a footballer, and being not quite good enough to make it.

Still . . . *we* made it! All of us . . . and N. McCann Super Star, Ace Demon, Top Striker, Goalscoring King with World Cup Potential made it! A Cup-winner's medal, and goals and goals and goals and lots more goals to come!

I know everybody can't win, but it feels really brilliant when you do . . . and we all reckoned it was just the first time.

We'd be back, and we'd do it again!